THE MAN WHO WOULDN'T TALK

Books by Quentin Reynolds

THE WOUNDED DON'T CRY

LONDON DIARY

CONVOY

ONLY THE STARS ARE NEUTRAL

LEAVE IT TO THE PEOPLE

THE MAN WHO

RANDOM HOUSE

NEW YORK

WOULDN'T TALK

by Quentin Reynolds

To David George and Glenn Maurice—
whose father was a gentle spy

THE MAN WHO WOULDN'T TALK

CHAPTER 1

Muriel DuPre stood on the railroad platform at Winnipeg, waiting for the train that was bringing her husband George home to her. It was August 15, 1946, and he had been gone since early 1940. These had been five long, lonely years, but now they were over and she would have him with her for the rest of their lives. The war had been much harder on most of her friends, she reflected: their husbands had been fighting in the desert in North Africa, in Italy, in Normandy; a great many had been killed on the hazardous Dieppe raid and others taken prisoner. She at least had been spared the mental agony of knowing that her husband was fighting.

Happily, George DuPre had been too old for

combat. He had spent his war at various RAF stations in England in some clerical capacity, the exact nature of which he had never quite explained. His letters were rather vague as to just what his duties had been; his letters, in fact, had been very unsatisfactory and she would tell him so, too. But then George had never been one for writing letters.

She heard the whistle of the locomotive and her excitement grew. In a matter of minutes now her soft-spoken, gentle husband would be with her. If there was a word for George that was it—gentle. She could never imagine George, with his slow good nature and his strong sense of religion, actually fighting a war. Thank God the military authorities had had the good sense to realize that and had given George an administrative job far from the front. George was brave enough; he'd spent thirteen lonely winters in the Arctic hunting and trapping, and it took courage to brave those dark northern winters alone except for the Eskimos. But she couldn't imagine her soft-eyed husband ever firing a gun in anger; anger and hatred were completely foreign to his nature.

The train roared into the Winnipeg station and men in khaki and gray tumbled out of the cars. Then through a mist of happy tears she saw him.

George DuPre stepped off the train, blinked a moment in the glare of a hot Winnipeg sun, and then his wife's arms were around him and for the first time in nearly six years everything was all right. She held him at arm's length, admiring the Air Force blue of his uniform; she exclaimed over the two rings on his arm which showed that he'd been promoted to Flight Lieutenant, and then she threw her arms around him again. His Air Force cap fell off and her eyes opened wide in shocked amazement.

"But, darling, your hair has turned white," she said.

It had been light brown when he left Canada early in 1940. He had first noticed the change in 1943, a few days after the Gestapo had released him from their Saint-Lô headquarters.

"It's that English sun." He laughed. "I went 'round bareheaded, and the sun bleached my hair."

She grasped his arm and led him to a waiting car. They sat in the car, each too filled with happiness to say much. Muriel DuPre held his right hand hard and noticed that he winced. She gazed down at the hand she knew so well and saw that the index finger was crooked; it looked as though it had been smashed and had been badly set.

"What happened, darling?" she asked.

He looked at the finger and the muscles of his stomach tensed. For a moment the finger was clamped in a vise again as the incessant voices snarled, "Who in Torigni leads the underground?"

and he had kept mumbling, *"Je ne sais . . . je ne sais,"* and then . . .

"We played a lot of football in England," George DuPre said to his wife. "Some clumsy RAF type stepped on my finger."

"You know, darling, your voice has changed," she said anxiously. "We were married eleven years before you joined up, and if there's one thing I know it's your voice. Have you had a sore throat?"

He nodded. Yes, his throat had been sore after they'd inserted a clamp into his mouth to hold it open and after they'd poured boiling water down his throat. It had been very sore for a long time. When his job had been finished and he had returned to England the plastic surgeons had worked long and patiently to repair the hopelessly burned tissues of his mouth and the infected bone of his jaw, but it was still difficult to pronounce some words.

"That English climate is so changeable," he muttered. "I was always getting colds and sore throats."

He told her very little, during that first month, of the part he had played in the war. The war was over and gradually—oh, very gradually—the nightmares were leaving him and life was beginning to run along an even course. He thought and talked only of the future, because that's where he and

Muriel were going to live. He learned that the Boy
Scouts could always use leaders, and when he volunteered to help, his services were accepted gladly.
They never knew, of course, that this was a pledge
he had made to himself as he lay in the filthy
Gestapo prison at Saint-Lô watching the men
in gray uniforms perform almost unspeakable
cruelties. It was then that he had decided to devote
the rest of his life to seeing that the kids in his home
town were never brought up to be insensitive
brutes. Occasionally in those first weeks the past
did intrude. A friend would say, "Straighten up,
George. You walk like an old man. What's the
matter—you got a weak back?"

The pain—except for the memory of it—had
gone now. He thought fleetingly of the day they
had spread-eagled him face down on an operating
table. Then a girl—she couldn't have been more
than twenty-three—had walked into the room
carrying a large syringe, the kind you use to in-
ject horses when you want to kill their pain. But
they hadn't wanted to kill his pain. The girl,
calmly as though she were a nurse on an errand of
mercy, had ripped the back of his trousers open
with a pair of shears and had then . . . George
tried to shake the memory of it out of his mind.

"Yes," George DuPre said, straightening up, "I
had a little trouble with my back. Just a wrench;
it'll be all right in a day or two."

Other returning veterans came home and they'd gather at the DuPre home and they'd tell of their experiences in North Africa and Italy and in the final slashing advance toward Berlin. George DuPre never said much. He had always been a quiet man —thirteen winters in the Arctic solitudes when he had been younger had given him the gift of silence. But gentle George DuPre was loved by his neighbors, and it was inevitable that they press him for details. In what theatre of operations had he spent the war?

"George sent me fifty-five letters in the five and a half years he was away," Muriel DuPre said, while laughing, "and he never told me where he was stationed. They were the most unsatisfactory letters. I only knew that he was somewhere safe in the North of England with the RAF. I was so glad that George was too old to fly. He was thirty-six when he joined up . . ."

"I spent most of my time with RCAF units in the north," a neighbor said curiously. "Odd we never ran across each other."

"I went to the Air Ministry in Whitehall," another said, "to find out where you were. They weren't very helpful. They said you moved from one air base to another."

"They kept moving me around," George DuPre mumbled a little desperately. Why didn't they stop? But after all, they were his friends—his best friends.

Then there was the evening which began, prosaically enough, by a visit to the movies but which ended with George in a state of collapse. On their way home they were chatting about the picture when they came abreast of a police station. A patrol wagon drew up and two cops pulled a protesting, hysterical drunk from the wagon. The drunk cried for help and Muriel felt George's hand tighten on her arm; she felt him tremble, saw him turn white, and then he slumped to the pavement in a dead faint. She bent over him frantic with worry, and then his eyes fluttered open and he murmured thickly and in accents she could hardly understand, *"Pourquoi me frappez-vous?"* Muriel, puzzled and anxious, said, "No one is beating you, darling. Tell me what's the matter." His eyes cleared then and he shook his head sheepishly and arose on unsteady legs. "The sight of that poor man being dragged to jail—it scared me," he said evasively.

Muriel looked at him thoughtfully. She had spent three winters in the Arctic with her husband, eighty miles from the nearest settlement. They had been three wonderful years, made wonderful because George was never afraid of the constant threat which the North holds over you during the freeze-up. And his great strength had kept her from fear. Now George had fainted at the sight of a drunk being hauled into the police station. She was puzzled and a little worried.

A week later he had gone to the military hospital for an operation on his nose. It had been a long operation and she had waited outside the operating room until it was over. When the white-robed surgeon (a colonel) came out, she asked, "How is my husband?"

"Fine, just fine," the doctor beamed. "Actually the other two operations laid the groundwork for us. We just had to finish up."

"The other two operations?" she faltered.

"The two they had to perform when he returned to England," he said casually. "Yes, considering what he went through these past five years he's in good shape."

"What he went through?" she repeated, bewildered—but he was gone.

Sometimes at night she'd lay beside him sleeplessly, hearing him muttering uneasily. George never slept quietly any more. On this night he suddenly cried out sharply, as though in great pain, *"Je ne sais pas."* She didn't recognize his voice; it was thick, blurred, and, looking at him, she saw that his lower jaw had fallen open and now his hands were moving aimlessly as though there was no co-ordination between them and his mind. *"Je ne sais pas,"* he cried out in anguished tones, and then she put her arms around him and noticed that his body was trembling. What horrible nightmare had gripped him? It had transformed him completely. He moved restlessly, moaning now as though he were being tortured.

"It's all right, darling, it's all right," she soothed him, and then his body relaxed and his eyes opened.

"I had a nightmare," he said in a low voice.

"I know. I know." She held him closer. "What is it, George? You've been hiding something, living alone with some awful memory. It isn't like you to keep secrets from me."

He sat up, wide awake now. "You're right. I didn't want to talk about it or think about it. But maybe I should tell you. . . ."

"Tell me what?"

"Those fifty-five letters," he said. "I couldn't say much in them. Actually they were all written back in 1940. They were really written by British Intelligence. I just copied what they told me to write and every few weeks they mailed one to you. You see, darling, I wasn't anywhere near a mail box during the war."

"But where were you?" she asked, bewildered.

"I spent the first four years in a village near Saint-Lô in Northern France," he said. "I worked with the French underground. And then I joined a group of forced laborers and got into a German submarine plant in Hamburg. My orders were to sink the German subs before they got wet. And finally . . ."

"You were a spy all during the war?" she gasped.

"Honey," he pleaded, "we never use the word 'spy.' We use the word agent. I was a British agent."

She sat up in bed, completely dumfounded. Her gentle, quiet, religious husband a spy? And then the little incidents which had puzzled her began to take on new significance. There was a nasty scar on his chin which he never talked about. There was the odd way he sometimes talked, almost as though English were an unfamiliar tongue to him. There was the white hair, the crooked finger, the operation and the long silences when his thoughts seemed to be far away.

She put her arms around him, held him tightly and said, "Tell me all about it, darling. You've held everything in for so long. Tell me—tell me why they picked you to be a spy."

"Agent," he corrected, unhappily.

"All right, agent," she smiled. "Now begin at the beginning . . ."

CHAPTER 11

They told him he was too old to fly when he volunteered for the RCAF, but they accepted him. At thirty-six he was slim and hard, and his ruddy face had the perpetual windburn you acquire if you live for long periods in the Arctic. He had very pale blue eyes, a square chin, and he smiled easily. He was a good listener too, and the pilots and crewmen with whom he trained at Toronto found it easy to confide in him. He was assigned to the Intelligence section; he would eventually go overseas with a flying unit and his job would be to hear the reports made by pilots who had returned from their missions. Six months later he found himself in England with the RCAF.

One day his C.O. asked him rather casually if

he'd like to transfer to an Intelligence unit of the RAF. "Might be interesting," the C.O. said, and George said he didn't care much one way or the other. The next day he was sent to London, told to report to a Mr. Jones at a Whitehall address. Mr. Jones, a civilian, was a genial, friendly soul who told George to sit down and have a cigarette.

"I've been studying your record for some time," the genial Mr. Jones said.

"But my outfit only arrived here three weeks ago," DuPre said uncertainly.

Mr. Jones nodded. "Yes, I know," he said dryly. "But your record was forwarded to us from Toronto some months ago. It may be that you're the man we're looking for to do a particular job of work. Mind if I ask you a few questions? Suppose we do it over a cup of tea."

Tea was brought in and Mr. Jones asked him a few casual questions about his early life. Sometimes when George's memory failed, the man named Jones prompted him. He knew that he had obtained the French-sounding name from Huguenot ancestors 200 years ago. Jones knew that he'd been born in Poona, India, and that his father had been Colonel Peter DuPre of the Royal Artillery. He led George through his childhood travels; every three years officers of the Royal Artillery were shifted to another garrison. The DuPre family had lived at Malta, at Gibraltar, on the Isle of Wight.

"That's when you joined the Boy Scouts, wasn't it?" Jones smiled.

George DuPre looked startled. "Yes, sir, but that was 'way back in 1914."

"Actually it was 1915, when you were eleven," his host corrected quietly. "And you and the other members of your scout troop acted as air wardens. When the Zeppelins and the German planes headed for London you lads went out on your bicycles and your bugles warned of the air raid. We didn't have sirens in that other war."

Mr. Jones recalled that George had gone through Harrow and Cambridge and then he lifted some papers from his desk—there was George's long-forgotten Cambridge record. It had been a fair record; nothing startling but at least sound.

"I imagine you'd seen enough of Army discipline," his genial inquisitor mused. "Your whole life—except for Cambridge—had been spent in Army garrisons. Quite restricted life for a healthy English youngster with imagination. Your father was a little unhappy because you wanted no part of an Army career, but when you said you wanted to make your own way in Canada he didn't object much. Your mother took a dim view of it, though. She thought it strange; here she'd sent you to Cambridge and you came out of the Old School—I was Cambridge, by the way, DuPre—interested only in the exploits of the Royal Canadian Mounted Police and with an intense interest in the Polar regions."

"How do you know . . ." George DuPre was completely dumfounded.

Jones smiled. "So you went to Canada. You headed north and worked on ships owned by the Hudson Bay Company. Let's see, now—your first job was deckhand on the *Distributor*. But soon you became a first mate and you pushed freight north down the Mackenzie, and then they gave you one of those forty-foot river boats. You used to run the rapids to get supplies into the Great Bear Lake. You liked the North enormously. During the winter when the lakes and the rivers were frozen over you always went off on your own to trap white foxes. The farther north you went, the better you liked it. You spent thirteen winters in the Arctic living alone or with the Eskimos. You're one of the few to really learn their language. Incidentally," he smiled, "you made quite a job of losing your Cambridge accent. After three years you became a Canadian citizen. I know you loved Canada so much you didn't want to be mistaken for an Englishman, so you set out deliberately to erase your accent. I must say not a trace of it remains."

"Forgive me, sir," DuPre asked, "but what has this to do with . . ."

"A great deal," the officer said. "To begin with, not many men can learn to live alone as you did those thirteen winters in the North. Man is a gregarious animal. It is seldom we find one who has resources within himself that he can draw upon to fight loneliness. You have strong spiritual resources within you, DuPre. You were never lonely in the North. When the ice broke you'd return South and there was always a place waiting for you with the Hudson Bay Company. They gave you increasingly important jobs. As early as 1930 you were investigating the possibilities of inland fishing for the company. But you'd always go north in the winter. Something drew you there."

DuPre nodded. Mr. Jones talked casually of the report George had given the company on the commercial possibilities of establishing a huge muskrat ranch in Manitoba. It was such a fine report, he chuckled, that the Manitoba Government had decided to make a relief project out of it. The Government had borrowed George from the company to organize the million-acre ranch.

"It was about then you married," Jones said, sipping his tea. "And now you brought your wife to the North and she learned to love it too."

"You . . . you know more about me than I know about myself," George said ruefully.

"I dare say we do," Jones said casually. "When we are looking for a man to do a particular job we —well, we investigate him pretty thoroughly."

"When you say 'we' who do you mean?" George asked curiously.

"The British Intelligence Service," Jones said simply. "We think you could be of use to us. Would you like to try our training course? If everything works out . . . we have quite an interesting job for you."

"But how can I be of use?" George was honestly bewildered. He'd always thought of himself as something of an average man. He didn't feel that he had any special talents that would qualify him to be a spy. "I'm not the type," DuPre said a little unhappily. "I've read about some of the exploits of your British agents . . ."

"DuPre, forget everything you've ever read about our service. It isn't glamorous; it isn't a job for a superman. Each man is assigned some small job that as often as not is quite humdrum and dreary. He may not even know why he is doing his particular task. But back here we assemble all the bits and pieces gathered from all our men and we fit them all into a picture, and that complete picture sometimes gives us something important. We think you are the type for our kind of work, DuPre."

CHAPTER III

Three days later George Dupre found himself sitting in another office—the office of Colonel William Baker, in charge of the Oxford Home for Convalescents. That's what the people of nearby Oxford called it. The main building had once been a baronial mansion; it was surrounded by five hundred acres of wooded land. People who approached too closely were warned away by friendly gardeners and gamekeepers. "Some of our patients are mental cases; they get violent," they'd say, shaking doleful heads. "Best stay clear of the place."

The gardeners and gamekeepers were all trustworthy Intelligence men, and the Oxford Home for Convalescents was actually one of the really top-secret installations in England; it was the training school for British agents. Tall, fifty-year-old Colonel Baker, handsome and with the same casual, genial manner of Mr. Jones, explained this to George DuPre over the inevitable cup of tea. He explained that George would have to undergo a vigorous nine-month training course. Among other things, he would study short-wave radio operation, the architecture of French bridges and viaducts, the strength, the vulnerability and the operation of French railroads; he would learn how to manufacture and handle explosives of all kinds; he would be taught how to care for and use pigeons as messengers; he would learn everything there was to learn about French automobiles; he would take a course on French police procedure, and would be trained in the art of parachuting from a plane.

"Then, of course," Baker said casually, "you'll be working constantly on your French and the usual Commando courses in silent killing."

"Silent killing?" George asked.

Colonel Baker nodded. "My dear chap, one of the easiest things in the world is to kill a man. No trick to that at all. But you will be taught to kill a man silently, so quietly that a sentry standing fifteen feet away won't know that anything is wrong. The particular job we have in mind for you may not involve any killing at all—we hope not—but one must be prepared. You agree?" he asked almost anxiously, as though wanting to please George DuPre.

"Of course." George found himself hypnotized by this man who talked so casually of killing.

"But all this is mere routine." Baker shrugged his shoulders. "This, let us say, is your basic training as an agent. Beyond this you must learn to take on the personality of a thirty-seven-year-old French garage mechanic who has an eight-year-old mind. This presents something of a problem," he admitted a bit dolefully. "But I think you can do it."

George blinked, but if casualness was the mood of the British Intelligence Service he would play along—get into the spirit of it and match casualness with nonchalance.

"When do I begin?" he said in what he hoped was a bored, disinterested voice.

Baker nodded approvingly. "Good show. Good show. You begin in a few moments. For nine months you will be trained for just one job. You are to be dropped into France, where you are to organize an escape route for air crews which have been shot down. You will work with the French underground and your headquarters will be in the village of Torigni, not far from Saint-Lô. You will act as liaison between the resistance group in that vicinity and our London office. You will not, at least not immediately, engage in any sabotage or any killing; yours is a rescue mission. Your job is to

save the lives of British airmen who have been shot
down and help them return to this country."

"I like that idea," George DuPre said thoughtfully. He wondered briefly if he could actually kill
a fellow man in cold blood—even a German. It
didn't look as if he would be put to the test. This
was a rescue mission. Fleetingly he thought of times
when he and a couple of Eskimos had lashed their
huskies north toward some lonely spot where a
trapper had been reported to be marooned. A rescue
mission? Yes, he liked the sound of it.

"I'll give you a day to think it over," Baker said
cheerfully. "You see, in our show, once you agree
. . . Well, you're committed."

"I don't need any time to think it over, Colonel.
I'm ready now."

Baker nodded happily. "Well, then. I'll give you
the gen." The "gen" was a word with which George
was already familiar; even his Canadian Air Force
colleagues had talked of orders as the "gen." "From
now on you are to think of yourself as Pierre Touchette who was born in the village of Torigni on
August 10, 1903. Your parents, Marcel and Madeline Touchette, really never should have married,"
Baker said sadly. "You see, they were first cousins,
and they thought the discredited law of consan-
guinity caught up with them. You—their only
child—turned out to be feeble-minded. Quite a sad
case, you agree?"

George DuPre agreed again. "I'm to impersonate Pierre Touchette?"

Baker nodded carelessly. "Monsieur Touchette, his wife and their unhappy half-wit son moved from Torigni in 1934. They moved north. The father never remained in one place too long. I suspect he felt a deep sense of shame because his defiance of natural laws had resulted in bringing a mentally deficient offspring into the world. Anyhow, the little family was caught in the rush of the German offensive in the very early days of the war, and all three were killed. The body of young Pierre was never officially found, so he is still listed as missing. Now if he were alive, it is quite possible— we have this on the authority of our top psychiatrists—that he would somehow make his way back to the village in which he was born. Freud explains that theory very convincingly. So when you show up, no one will think it too strange."

"But won't I be recognized?"

"No one in the village has seen Pierre Touchette since 1934," Baker reassured him. "It happens that you resemble him superficially, which is good enough for our purposes. Oh, there are one or two in the village who might know Pierre. There is an old doctor who brought him into the world, and the man who runs the local garage—you Canadians would call it a filling station—they might recognize Pierre. But do not worry about them."

23

"Are they . . ."

Baker held up his hand. "No sense in knowing too much, is there?" He laughed. "It is very unlikely that you will be picked up by the Germans when you are dropped, but if they do pick you up, you'd feel more comfortable not knowing the names of any of those who are helping us. You agree?"

George DuPre was so impressed with Colonel Baker that he would have agreed to almost anything he said. It all seemed so easy when Baker presented it in his informal way.

"Now the time has come for you to meet your shadow." Baker smiled and pressed a button on his desk. "Your shadow is, by a happy coincidence, an English counterpart of Pierre Touchette. He is thirty-seven and he has the mind of an eight-year-old. For the next nine months he will live with you, eat with you, sleep with you, dress with you, talk with you, play games with you. Gradually we hope that you will become a reasonable replica of Johnny Peterson, who, allowing for the fact that he doesn't speak French, is a reasonable replica of Pierre Touchette. Your French, incidentally," Baker said happily, "isn't too good, is it?"

"No," George said, "but I'll improve . . ."

"Heaven forbid," Baker laughed. "An eight-year-old boy has rather a limited vocabulary. You will be taught the accent peculiar to Normandy, but when you are speaking French—we have three

days a week here when no English at all is spoken
—remember you are not a member of the Academie
Française. Ah, here is our good friend Johnny Peterson."

Johnny Peterson walked into the office. He didn't
really walk—he skipped into the office. His eyes
fell on some flowers in a glass on Baker's desk and
he reached eagerly for them. "For Johnny—for
Johnny?" he pleaded.

"Yes, they're for you, Johnny," Baker said gaily.
"And this is your new friend Pierre. You have said
you had no one to play with, no one to help you
gather flowers. Pierre here will play with you and
will walk with you in the woods, and, Johnny, if
you're a good boy, I think Pierre may get you some
electric trains."

Johnny Peterson looked suspiciously at George
DuPre, but George smiled, nodded reassuringly and
said, "Yes, Johnny. You and I will be great friends.
And I'll try to get you some trains."

"I have blocks," Johnny Peterson said breath-
lessly. "You can play with my blocks. And I have
a top. It spins."

George DuPre put his arm around Johnny's
shoulders. "We'll get along fine," he said to Johnny
Peterson, but he was really talking to Baker. He
already felt a protective urge toward this gentle
child whom nature had hidden in the grotesque

body of an adult. "We'll get along fine," he repeated. Baker just said, "run along, you two, and get better acquainted. I'll meet you in the bar for a drink before dinner. And DuPre," he chuckled, "we'll get along fine too—I think."

C H A P T E R   I V

He found it easy to fall into the apparently hap-
hazard but actually intensely organized routine of
the training school. George learned that British
Intelligence was divided into several categories.
The colloquial term used by newspapers and the
public for the whole service was MI-5 (Military
Intelligence, Department No. 5). Actually MI-5
was the subdivision of Intelligence which concerned itself entirely with espionage. MI-3 was the
division which organized and carried out sabotage
operations, while MI-9 handled problems of escape. DuPre received training in all three depart-
ments, although he had been told that his primary
job would be MI-9 work.

One of the difficulties of aiding downed airmen

was that of identification. The airmen landing in hostile territory were apt to be suspicious of anyone who questioned them. Yet agents working with the underground could not pass an airman along to the next rescue point unless they were positive that the airman was in fact an Allied flier. Germans had successfully impersonated British and Canadian officers and had managed to destroy several rescue routes.

"One question which will trip a German masquerading as a Canadian officer," an instructor told George, "is, 'What ship did you cross the Atlantic on?' He'll either make up the name of a ship or refuse to give its name. If he refuses, youll have to think of something else, but if he gives you the name, you can check on him. Here is a list of every transport used in the Canadian service. Memorize it. It may come in handy some time."

The day began at six A.M. and you worked until dinner time. You'd assemble for a cocktail before dinner with your instructors and your fellow trainees, and then there would be lectures at night. Every man at the school was being trained for a particular job in occupied Europe or Germany, but all took the same basic training. The instructors always spoke of the task ahead as "a job of work." No one ever mentioned the word "danger"; no one ever suggested that most of these men were going to engage in the most hazardous activity in the world, with death the penalty of failure. Even the intensive course in silent killing (given by a Major in the Commandos) was done casually.

"You'll never have to use this stuff, old boy," he'd say grinning at George, "but you might as well know it. Might come in handy some day if your mother-in-law stays at your place too long." One group of six men were to be sent to do a quick job of killing the sentries and capturing a radar set on the French coast. George looked at these six young men in amazement. They were laughing, carefree young Englishmen, serious only when their instructors were teaching them some new method of killing quietly.

"What do you look for in men you pick for these difficult jobs?" George asked the instructor.

"Steady nerves," he said. "Fast reflexes. Good health. No experience in killing is needed," he added with a quick smile.

"Do you ever use gangsters or professional criminals?" George asked.

"Bless you, no," the Major said in a shocked voice. "They'd be no jolly good at all. Don't have the guts. Criminals usually kill out of fear or panic. To our men killing is a job of work. Matter of fact," he added soberly, "some of our best men are very religious. You really can't have guts without God."

"You can't have guts without God," George repeated slowly. That made great sense to him. He'd never quite articulated his own religious philosophy, but that seemed to sum it up pretty well. George remembered men with whom he had hunted and trapped foxes in the North. The bravest had been men of faith. The most courageous, self-sacrificing man he'd ever known had been an Eskimo up in King William's Land. He'd been devoutly religious, this Eskimo. The missionaries had converted him as a child, and to him God was a friendly, ever-present being who never failed you when early ice had sent the seals away; when there wasn't a bit of pemmican or dried caribou meat for many miles; when a blizzard had changed the known world into a trackless, frightening jungle of ice. He had God and he had guts. George remembered. Yes, this made sense—great sense.

All of the instructors stressed one point incessantly. "The success of your job depends upon implicit obedience to orders. When you are in enemy country you will often receive orders that seem silly. But every order has been carefully thought out. Obey them." Now and then a visitor would lecture to them. He might begin by saying, "I had an experience in Paris two nights ago that might prove useful to you men." And then he'd

tell of some extraordinary feat with complete nonchalance. You were encouraged to question these
men who had actually been working as agents in
enemy territory. Without exception they'd end
up by saying confidently, "Nothing to worry about.
It's a job of work like any other job. You get some
orders now and then that seem pretty foolish. But
these chaps back here know the score. You're never
really alone over there, not as long as you have
that little radio cached away somewhere. Funny
thing about this business. You've got to learn to
trust people. The brass hats back here tell us whom
to trust. Lord, I've been told to put my faith in
ten-year-old kids, in eighty-five-year-old great-
grandmothers, in surly, filthy sewer rats, and none
of them ever let me down. These chaps back here
know their business," he'd add cheerfully.

It was magnificent psychology, and gradually
George DuPre too began to think of his assignment as just a "job of work." A supreme air of
confidence radiated from the instructors and communicated itself to the trainees. Nothing seemed
impossible to this incredible organization called
so prosaically the BIS.

There were twenty-seven men training for various missions at the school. Some spoke with the
broad accent of Yorkshire; others in the unmistak-
able tones of the Oxford graduate. Some were uni-
versity professors, or graduate students; others,

business men who had spent long periods in Germany or France. Two of them were actors and one had come directly from a divinity school. They seldom talked of the missions to which they had been assigned; each lived alone with that. Gradually George found the common denominator which characterized them all. These were men of character; quiet men with a strong spiritual sense. Nearly all were churchgoers.

None had come directly from civilian life. All had gone through intensive training in Army, Commando, Navy or Air Force; most had been tested in the fires of combat. In some ways these twenty-seven men (and those who had been graduated and were now behind enemy lines) were the pick of Great Britain's armed forces. Sheer courage wasn't enough; they were men with flexible minds who could, if need be, improvise when all accepted methods of escape or evasion had failed. But they were taught to improvise only in the direst extremity. The training was designed to cover almost any emergency that might ever arise.

They were taught the difference between the German military mind and the mind of the Gestapo. If caught by the Gestapo they had to sustain the roles which they had been acting, no matter what the torture. "Just tell us the names of your accomplices," the Gestapo would say, "and we promise to let you go." Some had fallen for this line; they had immediately been killed. No matter what the torture, it had to be endured if only in the interests of eventual self-preservation. They were taught every trick the Gestapo used to loosen a man's tongue.

During their free hours George noticed that most of them visited the well-stocked library. Several of them were interested in poetry, and George would listen with fascination as they discussed the relative merits of Yeats and Eliot. As they sat in the beautifully paneled library in front of a roaring fire they never talked of the day's training in killing or sabotage. All were gradually absorbing the philosophy of their new trade. "It's a job of work," and when the business of the day was done they relaxed and tried to forget the instructions given by Commando officers or experts in the use of dynamite.

Some, like George, were developing entirely new personalities. They all watched with interest the experiment being tried on Archie Steele. Steele was to impersonate a deceased Frenchman. The man whose place he was to take had one physical deformity that made impersonation a bit difficult. His right leg was an inch and a half shorter than his left leg. Steele, who had been a high-school teacher in civilian life, became increasingly proud as the doctors gradually shortened his right leg.

"You see, DuPre," he said earnestly, "we're all four inches taller than we have to be. If you could take some kind of a giant press and clamp it down on us we could all lose four inches and never know the difference. Our bones don't actually fit snugly into sockets. They fit loosely, with a little cushion of space between bone and socket. Now they've put a cast around my middle and one around my right thigh. These are connected by springs. Every other day they increase the tension a little more. I've already lost a full inch," he said proudly, "and have only half an inch to go."

In civilian life Samuel Rosen had been an estate agent, collecting rents and managing the affairs of one of England's largest country properties. He would be dropped into Germany to impersonate a German officer, a war prisoner whom Rosen resembled to a startling degree. His problem was completely lingual; the German officer stammered badly, and Rosen had a shadow who took ten minutes to pronounce any word with an "s" in it.

No one was allowed to leave the grounds, but the recreational facilities were excellent. There was a well-stocked bar, differing from the bar of a luxury hotel only in the fact that no bills were ever presented. You could have anything you wanted, but these men never took more than an occasional gin-and-tonic or a Worthington lager. The food was excellent, the billiard room as good as you'd find in any London club; there was a private golf course on the grounds, and tennis courts were available. And every day George DuPre learned more about radio and the codes which had to be memorized. He learned about French architecture and railroads and the French peasant idiom and the intricacies of French automobiles, and he came to know explosives—and he learned the art of silent killing. Gradually, too, he was aping every move made by Johnny Peterson. Once a week a Harley Street pyschiatrist visited the school to note George's progress. "You're too neat at dinner table," he'd growl. "Always spill some of your soup. Never use a knife to push food onto your fork; use your fingers. Always keep your hands moving, not jerkily but slowly, aimlessly. Keep your mouth open. Drop your lower jaw, man. Your speech is too crisp. We must do something about that."

He did. He gave George a round pebble and told him to toss it into his mouth when he awoke each morning. He was to remove it only when he was eating. For three months he carried the pebble in his mouth. Gradually his speech became slurred. It was hard to form words with the tongue thus hindered by a pebble, but somehow the words, a bit misshappen but recognizable, did emerge from the larynx. It was seven months before the doctor was satisfied. But then he gave George the supreme accolade.

"If I met you today for the first time," he said, happily, "I'd stake my professional reputation that you had an eight-year-old mentality."

They would run in the woods together. John liked to play that he was a locomotive and George the train. George would grab him by the waist and they would chug around the trees, with John uttering a loud "toot-toot" in simulation of a locomotive whistle. For weeks George was self-conscious in his play with the idiot. Then gradually he found himself enjoying the childish games. He knew then that he was winning this psychological fight to adopt the mental attitude of the boy.

At first he thought a lot of his past life in the Arctic, of the wonderful three years he and Muriel had in a log cabin eighty miles from the nearest settlement, and of the trapping and hunting they had done, and of long, companionable nights before a fire with the frozen world outside intensifying their closeness. But as the weeks lengthened into months he seldom thought of his days in Canada. It was as though the past were somehow receding, and what had happened to him as George DuPre were things that had happened to someone else entirely. The reality was Pierre Touchette. Everything else was becoming a dim memory, dropping into the smothering mist of his subconscious.

Now George entered the final phase of his training. They took away his uniform and gave him the kind of clothes worn by the French villagers of Normandy. He became accustomed to the heavy boots, the baggy trousers, the black cotton jersey and the peaked cap of the peasant. They showed him how the hard peak of the cap could be used as a weapon. It was an old trick of the Liverpool Irishmen who had once been forced to fight so hard for their jobs and their very lives when they came to work on the Liverpool docks half a century ago. You merely sewed a razor inside the peak with the cutting edge facing out. If you were stopped by an enemy and if you were carrying anything so valuable that elimination of the enemy was called for, you merely ducked your head quickly, taking care that the peak of your cap hit his jugular vein.

"Just a trick of the trade," his instructor said cheerfully. "You'll never have to use it, Pierre, but these things are nice to know."

They all called him Pierre now. He'd almost forgotten what it had been like to be George DuPre. He had been married to Muriel in 1935, and until now he'd never withheld a secret from her. Now when he wrote her, Colonel Baker went over his letters. "This is the Silent Service, you know." He'd laugh. "Why not let us write your letters home? We're quite good at it. You just copy them in your handwriting and she'll never know the difference."

"For God's sake," George protested. "I love my wife."

"So do I, DuPre," Baker said sadly. "But I can't open my heart to her. She thinks I'm on some mission in South America. And damn it, DuPre, she lives only eighty miles from here."

"Combat service has its advantages," George said a little bitterly.

Baker nodded. "Yes, but perhaps in our own way we can contribute something. Trust us in small things like the writing of letters home, DuPre. Trust us and perhaps some day . . ."

"I trust you more than any man I ever met," George said simply.

Then suddenly George was no longer served the fine meals which had been such a pleasant part of his first few months at the school. Now he was served the kind of food Pierre Touchette would be expected to eat in Torigni. Instead of water he had to drink a cheap *vin ordinaire* at all meals. Sometimes they served him a raw Calvados or Framboise. The only meat he was given was horse meat. George didn't mind that. For thirteen years in the Arctic he'd lived on the frozen fish, salted venison and blubber of the Eskimo. He was given black bread and made to drink the ersatz coffee which had been the conquerors' gift to occupied

France. He began to look forward now to the great adventure. There was no feeling of tension, for the very casual Colonel Baker and his impassive instructors refused even to imply that the slightest degree of danger would be involved on his mission. It was "just a job of work."

One day Baker gave him a bottle of engine oil and told him to rub it thoroughly into his boots and his clothes. "This is the type oil they use around Saint-Lô," he said. "In case you should mislay these clothes and they were to be found and examined by the Germans under a microscope they'd find nothing but the oil which any garage helper would have on his clothes in that district. And take this bag of dirt along," he added. "It's from a field outside Torigni. Before you leave rub it under your fingernails and into your hands and arms."

"When am I off?" George asked, but Baker, usually the most genial of men, only looked at him reproachfully. George mentally kicked himself. You never asked questions in this service. You only took orders. No one knew when his particular trip was scheduled. One morning Steele, whose leg had finally shortened to the right length, didn't appear for breakfast. They knew then that he was somewhere in France or Germany putting to use the things he'd learned here at the Oxford Home for

Convalescents. Two days later Rosen's place was vacant.

Now George's training was stepped up sharply. After nearly nine months he was expert in the use of short-wave transmission sets; he could handle a Sten gun, a machine gun or a hand grenade with equal facility, and assemble the first two blindfolded. Explosives were friendly substances now that he knew how to fondle them, and he knew the inside of every French car as well as the more common type of German automobile. He knew how to send pigeons off with messages, and he had learned from agents who had returned from France every trick of communicating with resistance units in adjacent villages when all obvious routes had been blocked off. He knew a great deal about bridges and viaducts and railroads, and he had been taught the difference between the Gestapo and the regular German army intellect. And he had played endless hours with John Peterson learning to handle alphabet blocks and toy trains just as the poor dim-witted lad handled them. He no longer needed the pebble in his mouth to simulate the half-wit's manner of talking; it was second nature now to look, act and talk the part. He hadn't thought of himself as George DuPre for a long time; he was Pierre Touchette, whose parents had been killed by the Germans somewhere up north.

Then they sent George on long hikes carrying a

heavy load on his back. They made him run through the obstacle course and then, when breathless and aching with weariness he flung himself on the ground, they'd bark an order and make him do it all over again. His food for some mysterious reason had been cut to six hundred calories every twenty-four hours. This was kept up for five long days. Then one night after he had collapsed into a deep sleep he was awakened sharply. He found himself looking into the beam of a cruel bright flashlight that was only six inches from his eyeballs.

Wie heissen sie?" a voice barked.

"Je suis Pierre Touchette," he mumbled, more than half asleep.

What do you do? Where were you born? Where are your parents? One question followed another so quickly that he had no time to think—but he gave the answers Pierre Touchette of Torigni would have given. This was kept up for half an hour, and then the flashlight dimmed and the room lights flashed on. A grinning Colonel Baker slapped him on the shoulder. "Good show—good show," Baker said cheerfully, and then George DuPre realized that this had been his final test. They had purposely starved him and overworked him to the point of exhaustion in the hope of finding a weak point in his armor, if such weak point existed. But even semi-conscious he had kept his identity; he had been the mumbling, slightly incoherent Pierre Touchette of Torigni.

They gave him plenty of good red horse meat during the next few days, and then one afternoon Baker called him to his office. He chatted awhile about the training methods used and he talked about the British Intelligence Service.

"The newspapers call us the Silent Service," he chuckled. "Not bad—that. You've been damn well trained to do a job. You'll go over and do it and then what happens? Nothing. It's the Silent Service. No thanks, no medals, no public acclaim. You're just an unknown, anonymous British agent who has helped a little toward ending the war."

"That's good enough for me," George said fervently.

"You've written all those letters home?" Baker asked.

"That's for sure," George grinned. "Fifty-five of them."

"We'll see that she gets one every now and then. Your allotment will go to her every month. Don't worry about her. We try to take good care of our own."

George nodded. By now he had acquired the confidence and the pride in the service he had noticed in the veteran agents. He had acquired an enormous respect for this tall, clean-shaven, pleasant man named William Baker (if indeed that was his real name). And he felt that he had gone through the nine months' course with at least passing grades.

"You'll leave at 11:45 tonight," Baker said. "Looks like a nice night for flying."

"Three-quarter moon," George said, matching Baker's nonchalance. "Rather exceptional weather for February. It would be much colder back in Winnipeg."

"Well, here's the gen," Baker said. "It's quite simple."

He talked for two hours.

CHAPTER V

It wasn't much of a trip from the airfield attached to the school to the French coast. Neither the pilot of the single-engined Lysander nor his radio man said much to George DuPre as the plane slipped casually through a star-speckled night. George was in the rear gunner's cockpit. To the crew this was a routine trip; they soared over France nearly every night bringing some nameless, anonymous passenger to his hazardous destination. Often the passenger was dressed in the peasant clothes worn by George DuPre. As often as not he carried nothing in his pockets except the identity card and the few francs which DuPre was carrying. The Channel looked placid and the reflected moon gazed back from its calm surface. There were no lights on the coast nor beyond it, and George wondered how the pilot could find the one particular field where he, George, was to land.

"Nice moon," the pilot called to DuPre through the intercom. "Maybe too nice," he added.

Then, "Five minutes," the pilot called cheerfully.

The plane was flying low to escape the German radar screens.

"You'll jump at 1,200 feet," the pilot called. A moment later he cried, "Now jump," and DuPre hurled himself from the plane. As he did so he hit the metal disk on his chest that released the 'chute. It opened immediately and George looked up. He saw a friendly cloud hiding the moon, and then the ground rushed up to meet him. The routine of parachute instruction ran through his mind, and his muscles obeyed automatically. He hardly felt the jar as his feet touched the soft ground of the plowed field. He lay there a moment and then unfastened his 'chute. He gathered the black silk 'chute (agents were always dropped in black 'chutes) into his arms and it was as though Colonel Baker were there repeating his instructions.

"With luck you'll land in the center of the field. Go north and you'll find a hedge. Roll up your 'chute and hide it under that hedge. One of our friends will pick it up and bury it." He reached the hedge, pushed the 'chute under it and listened. The sound of the plane was growing fainter and fainter now, and then when it disappeared there was silence. "Follow the hedge east until it ends. Then strike off direct north. You'll hit the farm then." George followed instructions. Then the cloud having shielded him during the critical moments, revealed the moon again and in its white light George saw the outlines of farm buildings. "To the left will be the farmhouse—two floors. To the right two farm buildings—one a low building about twenty feet by ten. The other contains a hen house below and a hayloft above." They were there all right and George grinned appreciatively and thankfully. "Just obey orders, trust us to give you the proper directions," Baker had said. George advanced to the larger farm building. Here he should find a flight of steps leading up to the hayloft. "There should be fifteen steps; if there are more or less than fifteen, it means you've stumbled on the wrong farm," Baker had warned him. The steps were there. He ascended them quietly. There were exactly fifteen. He slipped into the softness of the sweet-smelling hay and lay there. The first and most important part of his mission had been completed. From now on the initiative would be taken by others. There was nothing for him to do now except relax and, if he could, sleep. He slept.

He awoke to the sound of clucking hens. Someone was down below feeding them. "At exactly six A.M. the farmer's wife will feed the chickens. Do not move until you hear her whistle the 'Marseillaise,'" Baker had said. He heard her moving around, scattering grain, and then he heard the whistled tune of the French national anthem. There was an opening leading to the lower part of the barn. He slid down and the chickens set up a startled cackling. A plump, middle-aged woman stood there looking at him reproachfully. She quieted the chickens and then George said, "*Fermez la porte.*" The woman straightened up and looked at him without expression. George felt a moment of panic. Those had been the three words of recognition, but her face showed neither understanding, welcome or interest. She merely beckoned with her head and walked out of the barn. He followed her to the house.

The kitchen was warm and cheerful. She motioned him to a seat. "Let them do the talking," Baker had warned him. "You'll think them unduly suspicious at first. Remember, before they give you their confidence, they have to check you carefully to see whether you've come from London— or Berlin." George remembered that now. He sat there silently and she served him a soft-boiled egg, two slices of black bread and a cup of ersatz coffee. She grimaced with disgust as some of his coffee slopped onto her clean tablecloth. He was Pierre Touchette now, the halfwit who spilled his food and who couldn't even handle a spoon properly.

When he finished she signaled him to follow her
upstairs. There were three bedrooms on the second
floor. She led him into one of them and he heard
the grate of the lock slipping into place. He undressed, climbed into the clean bed and fell asleep.
When he awoke a big, loose-jointed man with a
heavy mustache and a lined face was standing by
the bed. "You'll remain here two, maybe three
days," he said tonelessly, and then he left. The
plump woman brought him his meals but never
talked to him. Two days passed slowly, and then on
the morning of the third both of them came to his
room. The farmer's face wore a friendly smile now.
"Everything is all right," he said. "Here is your
ration card. You only need that and your identity
card. I will take you to Georges Lavelle now."

"Lavelle?"

"He owns the garage where you will work. He
expects you. By the way, my name is Joseph
Thibaut. My wife's name is Madeline."

The farmer walked boldly out of the house and
DuPre shambled behind. The village of Torigni
was only two hundred yards down the road. He
passed the post office; next to it was the church he
would soon know as St. Peter's, and standing on
the steps of the church was an elderly priest looking at him with almost too much of an appearance
of disinterest. He passed the courthouse and a
bakery, out of which came the sweet smell of fresh

bread. Across the cobbled street there was a harness maker's shop and a clothing store, and then the farmer stopped and there was the garage. Outside stood two gasoline pumps. A man was bending over a punctured tire. He straightened up and DuPre had his first look at Georges Lavelle. Like the farmer, he too was a big man with a thick crop of iron-gray hair. He smiled a welcome and said, "Ah, the son of my old friend Touchette. Good to see you, Pierre."

George nodded and grinned foolishly. "Come on, boy, I'll show you where you'll sleep," Lavelle said warmly. "Isn't much, but there's a stove and a cot." He walked through his small garage and opened a back door. George followed him. A ramshackle shed was attached to the back of the building. It wasn't much, as Lavelle had said. George didn't examine his new quarters closely. He felt he'd have plenty of time for that later; he didn't know then that this would be his home for the next four years. Lavelle chatted on aimlessly and then George realized that his talk wasn't aimless at all.

"You won't find any of the boys around you knew as a child, Pierre," he said. "All gone from the village by now. Some killed in the war, some captured, some moved to the coast. Old Doctor Rennet is still here, though. He brought you into the world; he's nearly eighty now, but he's a wonderful man. And Father Moduit is dead. Died right after you moved away. Father Gauraud took his place. Fine man. Mass is at seven every morning. You must go to church every morning, Pierre. Remember that."

He had underlined those words. Why must he go to church every morning? It sounded almost like an order. Perhaps it was an order. In any case, you had to learn to trust people; he would trust Georges Lavelle. The garage owner showed him how the gasoline pumps operated. Then he pointed down the street. "There's the shop where your father worked so many years ago," he said casually, pointing to the clothing store. "The blacksmith's forge is up the road a bit—you'll get to remember all the places you knew when you lived here."

George listened to the small, friendly sounds of the morning; the little laughs of women coming to market, the regular tread of shod hooves on the cobbled street, the happy barking of small dogs, the occasional triumphant crow of a rooster, the pleasant sound of a broom being vigorously swept across the grocer's sidewalk; the normal sounds of a small peaceful Normandy village getting ready for the day were comforting. It was hard to believe that he was in occupied France; that these people going so casually and cheerfully about their usual chores were conquered men and women. Which of them knew about him, George wondered. Which of them had accepted their fate—which were hiding a burning resentment and hatred of the Germans under the expressionless faces they turned to the soft sun which had now sent the early chill from the air?

Then the clatter of a car shattered the quiet of the morning. A large Mercedes screamed to a stop before the gasoline pumps and George had his first glimpse of the Gestapo. The officer sitting beside the driver barked out an order for ten liters of petrol. He hardly glanced at the vacant-faced idiot who unscrewed the gas cap and inserted the hose. George took a cloth and started to wipe the windshield. Lavelle walked out, nodded to the Gestapo officer and watched his new helper service the car. The officer stepped out of the car to stretch his legs. When the tank was filled, George replaced the hose and then again applied his cloth to the windshield.

The officer, impatient at his slowness, gave him a hard kick that straightened him up. His lower jaw dropped and he put on an appearance of complete bewilderment.

"*Ne fais pas attention à ce garçon. C'est un idiot,*" Lavelle said, shrugging his shoulders.

"An idiot." The Gestapo officer looked with distaste at the garage helper.

The car roared away and George DuPre felt an immense surge of happiness. He had passed his first test. Lavelle looked at him, clapped him on the shoulder and grinned appreciatively. A half dozen times cars driven by German officers and French gendarmes stopped for gasoline. Citroens, Mercedes, Opals, Renaults—back at the Oxford Home for Convalescents George had been taught the position of the gas cap on each of them; he had been taught how to lift the hood and he knew the location of the oil cap in each. "You act as though you'd been working here all your life," Lavelle said.

The next morning George went to mass. He reached the little church a few minutes before seven. The priest was standing in the church lobby talking with Lavelle, with the farmer Thibaut and his wife. "My new helper," Lavelle said, introducing George to the priest. Père Gauraud, a small, black-haired man dressed in a threadbare cassock, looked at George out of calm dark-blue eyes. "Pierre Touchette? Sad about your parents, son. I noticed in our old records that they were married here in this church and that you were baptized here. Ah, Madame Bouvot." A cheerful woman of sixty, her hair covered with a bright-blue shawl, patted Pierre on the head. "I knew your parents well, Pierre. You haven't changed much since you left us so long ago." George shuffled his feet and grinned in embarrassment. Madame Bouvot looked at him and then smiled, he felt, with silent approval. "*Eh, bien, le docteur est arrivé*," the little priest said.

Dr. Henri Rennet was nearly eighty. He was clean-shaven, his linen was clean and his white hair was combed meticulously. His long thin fingers and nails were clean. His skin, tightly drawn over his high cheekbones, was almost ivory, but his large eyes looked young and bold and his voice was strong. "Welcome, boy," he said, and George knew that he meant it. The next arrival was Albert Baudouin, whose leather apron, huge hands and bulging arm muscles marked him as the village blacksmith. The last man to join them was Gerard Benois, a jovial man who was introduced as the proprietor of Le Chien Noir, the village café.

George felt that they were all appraising him, waiting for him to speak. Nothing had been said, but he knew now that these were the men and women with whom he would work. Lavelle, the garage owner; Père Gauraud, whom George sensed to be the leader; the genial Madame Bouvot with her enormous oversize skirt and bright shawl; Dr. Henri Rennet; the Farmer Joseph Thibaut and his phlegmatic wife Madeline; the blacksmith Albert Baudouin; the café owner Gerard Benois. They were quiet now, standing in the dim coolness of the church, and then Père Gauraud said softly, "Is there anything you wish to say to us, Pierre?"

"Not now," George grinned, turning his head away shyly as Pierre Touchette would have done if addressed by the priest.

"Then I will begin mass," the little priest said.

Every morning the nine assembled in the rear of the church, chatted casually and then took their places in the pews. George never relinquished his role. Actually it was second nature now to play the halfwit; it would have taken a strong effort to assume the role of George DuPre. He pumped gasoline and made minor repairs to cars all day. He cooked his own meals on the stove in his little lean-to. Lavelle occasionally gave him a few francs with which he bought bread, cheese and horse meat. Two weeks passed and now the garage helper was accepted by everyone in the village and by the collaborating gendarmes and the Gestapo officers who stopped to re-fuel their cars.

A week passed and then late one night he was awakened by Lavelle. "We have picked up two British flyers," he said tensely. "At least they claim to be British flyers. They are at Josephe's farm. Will you come, please?"

Père Gauraud was waiting at the farm for George and Lavelle. The two pilots were in the room where DuPre had spent his first three days. They were very young; that was George's first impression, and they were a bit bewildered too, as a priest and an obviously mentally defective peasant walked into the room.

"Can't you get us on the Rat Run?" one of the young pilots said anxiously. The escape route lead-

54

ing to Torigni from villages farther inland and
from Torigni to Saint-Lô and from Saint-Lô to the
boats which would take them back to England, was
always referred to as the Rat Run by the RAF.

"Tell us who you are," the priest said in his halt-
ing English. They repeated their names, serial
numbers, and that was all. Where were you trained? What type aircraft do you fly? How many missions have you had? The two pilots looked contemptuously impassive at these questions.

"You know the gen, Padre," one of them said.
"Name and serial number; that's all we're required
to reveal to the enemy."

"But we are not the enemy," the priest said.

The pilots shrugged their shoulders. "Maybe
not," one of them said. "Maybe we have to take
each other on trust."

George whispered a few words into the ear of
Père Gauraud. The priest changed his line of questioning. "Tell me about Leicester Square in London," he asked.

"That's easy," one of them laughed. "I was born
in the West End. Leicester Square? Well, there's
the big Odeon Cinema and the '400' Club—that's
a bottle club, Padre—and . . ."

He described Leicester Square perfectly. DuPre
gave the priest a few more whispered instructions.
"Where is Skindles?" he asked, stumbling a bit
over the difficult word. "Skindles?" one of the pilots

laughed. "I was there only a week ago. It's on the Thames at Maidenhead. Jolly good pub it is, too. Not far from the Izaak Walton Inn. He's that chap who spent his life fishing. Nice part of the country, Maidenhead."

DuPre put his hand on the priest's shoulder and pressed it.

Père Gauraud smiled now and told the pilots they were satisfied. "We have to be careful," he apologized. "The Germans have been known to send their own English-speaking men to this territory in the hope of learning how we pass you boys on to the next safe spot."

"Who's this chap?" one of the pilots said, curiously, pointing to DuPre.

Just one of the villagers we use as a guide," the priest smiled, tapping his forehead significantly. "Now we'll furnish you with some clothes and set you off on the Rat Run. You will be guided to a farmhouse about two miles from here and someone else will take over."

"We're in your hands," one of the pilots said cheerfully. RAF pilots and crewmen had been briefed thoroughly as to the escape route. Once they were satisfied that they were in fact dealing with the Resistance, they had been told to trust their guides completely. The priest and George DuPre left the farm and walked back to the village.

During the next week Père Gauraud told George

a great deal more about the work of the underground. Each village had a "troop" of Resistance fighters. At the moment all were concentrating on aiding downed airmen to escape; later he said there would be other work to do. In Torigni there were the eight George had met in the rear of the church. This was the troop and of these only Thibaut, his wife, the priest and Georges Lavelle knew that George was a British agent. The troop used boys and girls and the very old as messengers to adjacent villages and to Saint-Lô, but these did not know the identity of any of the troop. George discovered that the transmission set was hidden in a deserted barn two miles outside the village, and he learned that contact with London had been established four times a week. Each week the transmitter was moved to another spot.

"Technically," the priest laughed, "we are members of DeGaulle's forces. Every Friday night a plane comes over to drop various things we have asked for; it also drops our soldiers' pay. We are merely one little troop. But in hundreds of villages there are similar little troops. London co-ordinates our efforts. We obey blindly, knowing that we are a link in the chain that leads to safety for your airmen."

A week later disaster struck the Torigni troop. Four girls between the ages of eleven and sixteen had been delivering messages from the village to

Saint-Lô. Each rode a bicycle, and the Germans had never suspected them. More than once Gestapo men had stopped and searched the girls, but had never found anything incriminating. Each had the perfect excuse for her trip. "I am visiting relatives in Saint-Lô," the girl would say, and because they never ventured forth after curfew there was no reason to suspect them. But the Germans knew that British airmen were being downed in this district and they knew that they were able to get their hands on very few of them. What happened to the others? Obviously there was some kind of an organized escape route, and the Gestapo had been sent into the area to find it and discover the Resistance members who were engaged in the work.

Messages were never handed directly to the girls by any of the nine members of the troop. They were left at the homes of the youngsters. The girls looked upon it all as an exciting game—never as a matter of life or death. Fooling the Germans was a game more stimulating, more fun, than any of the games they had played before the war. And besides, each of them received a fine bicycle; they never knew that the bicycles—exact replicas of the French-made wheels—had been dropped by British planes. There was just one difference between the standard bike and these; the left handlebar unscrewed. It was hollow and it was just large enough to hold written messages. One of the girls bicycling toward Saint-

Lô twelve miles away had a slight accident. Her bike had slid into a parked automobile. Unfortunately this was a Gestapo car. An officer about to enter it saw the girl sprawling on the roadside, and he saw something else too. He saw that the impact had knocked the left half of the handlebar loose. He picked it up and found a written message.

Within five days all four girls had been picked up and questioned. None knew anything; even torture couldn't make them reveal secrets which they didn't know. The Gestapo immediately shot the four youngsters. Père Gauraud told George of the tragedy. The little priest was heartsick; George couldn't afford to indulge in the luxury of emotion. The messenger service was absolutely essential to the success of the escape route. Orders received in the village had to be transported to other villages; to other links in the chain that led to freedom. The nine long months of training George had gone through now began to pay off. Obviously bicycles could not be used again—at least not for some months. The Gestapo mind was not flexible. The men in gray would have bicycles on their minds for a long time. No one on a bicycle would be safe from search and questioning. This was a situation which was almost routine to British Intelligence, and considerable time had been spent during the training course in the study of alternative messenger routes.

"Get four more girls," George DuPre said, "or two boys and two girls. Find four dogs and give each child one of them. The youngsters must feed these dogs, sleep with the dogs and make friends of them. Have our men make four dog collars, round leather collars. Messages can be concealed in these hollow collars. The youngsters can now walk to deliver the messages. The dogs will trail behind them. The Gestapo will never suspect a youngster with a dog. If they suspect the boy or the girl they will do nothing but search them; they will not think of searching the dogs."

Père Gauraud nodded appreciatively. He was glad, George sensed, to have some of the responsibility taken off his shoulders. He immediately hurried away to tell his men to fashion the collars and to collect four friendly dogs. Within eight days four girls and four dogs were skipping casually across the fields and along the roads and paths which led from Torigni to adjacent villages. The broken link had been replaced; the chain was again a strong, vital lifeline. Within the next two months thirty British airmen had been hurried along the Rat Run to safety.

London had forbidden George to send radio messages himself; the little priest had been trained in its use and it was he who went to the transmitter four nights a week to call London on a prearranged wave length. London kept a twenty-four-hour moni-

tor service alert. Usually there were messages for
C-193 (George's number was changed every few
weeks). But occasionally orders did come from the
unknown London headquarters. One night a warning came that the Germans were using a mobile
detecting unit which could spot a transmission set
when it was either sending or receiving. George
told the priest to keep moving the transmitter; to
keep it away from the roads and the German truck
with its detecting equipment. Messages came from
other villages saying that two transmission sets had
been discovered and captured. London, informed
of this, messaged laconically, "Dropping pigeons
Friday night." The drops were never on the same
field. London seemed to know more about the topog-
raphy of the area than local residents did. The
priest had a map showing every field in the district;
each had been given a number. London had a similar map. If London said that the next parachute
drop would be to Field No. 143, the priest by a
glance at his map knew just where he should send
Albert Baudouin, the blacksmith, and Gerard
Benois, the café keeper, to pick up the cargo. The
mystery of how the British pilots were able to pin-
point these small fields so accurately was explained
when the priest told George that a man with a flashlight was always stationed exactly one mile south
of the field to be used that night. The pilot and his
crew always flew low; as soon as the sound of their

engines was heard the man below began to blink his flashlight. The navigator was able to get an exact fix on that, and knew that the drop would be made exactly one mile north.

The pigeons arrived on the next drop. They were in light wire cages, weighted at the bottom so they would fall straight, and, to insure a soft landing, a two-inch rubber shock absorber was attached to the under part of the cages. They arrived in fine condition and were transported to a deserted barn five miles from the village. With the pigeons was a package of specially prepared paper for the writing of messages to be sent by the pigeon express. A rather cryptic message said that only misleading information should be sent by pigeon; the paper on which the messages were to be written should be thoroughly soaked in water and then attached to the pigeons. The paper was of a type that would disintegrate within three hours. George had no idea what headquarters was up to, but he remembered an instructor saying, "You get some orders now and then that seem pretty foolish. But these chaps back here know the score." So each night George would dictate misleading messages to the priest to be sent by the flying couriers. The messages would be water-soaked and then slipped into the small carrier receptacle attached to the leg of the pigeon. He received further orders to send the messages during the daylight hours. This seemed to invite detection, but then George realized that this was probably what London had intended all along. More pigeons were dropped; more misleading information sent—and then one day the priest reported sadly that the Germans had apparently discovered this new method of keeping in touch with London. They hadn't been able to locate the pigeon cote as yet, but they had noticed that a great many pigeons were flying a direct route to England, where before only the smaller Normandy birds had been seen in the air. The Germans had loosed falcons at the pigeons and the falcons had killed at least a dozen of them.

"Few of our messages got through." The priest looked glum.

"Tell London," George said. London's response completely puzzled the little priest. "Keep pigeons flying," was the order. They kept false messages winging toward England, the falcons attacked the helpless pigeons and slaughtered many, and then the supply of birds stopped. Operation pigeon was finished. Two Gestapo men who had lingered too long over their brandy at Le Chien Noir had been laughing about the stupidity of the Resistance troops in relying on pigeons.

"We got all of their radios," one boasted, "so they had to depend on pigeons. Now their pigeons are all gone and they have no contact with London at all."

When innkeeper Benois reported this at church the next morning, George chuckled. The "chaps back there" certainly did know their business. The pigeon experiment had been a decoy from the beginning, intended to be detected. Now the German mobile unit, satisfied that all sending sets in the area had been discovered, would move somewhere else. The priest finally understood, and his eyes twinkled as he told George. "My Bishop might not like it, but I think I will say a mass for those pigeons who died so nobly. After all, Saint Francis used to pray with the birds and pray for them, too."

CHAPTER VI

Père Gauraud was the unquestioned leader of the troop, commissioned as such by DeGaulle in London. But he had never had any real military experience. Only Thibaut, Lavelle and Baudouin the blacksmith had served in the army, but their technical knowledge was limited. DuPre was in the position of being an expert consultant to the troop, with the priest nominally in command. When the priest gave his orders at the back of the church, he ignored DuPre. When he was perplexed or had received specific orders for DuPre, he would go to the lean-to in back of the garage to discuss matters with George alone. When George decided upon a plan of action or when he thought some project of the priest's to be unsound, he would wait until he

could get the priest alone. This was all calculated
and according to orders laid down at the training
school. Had Madame Bouvot or Baudouin or Doctor
Rennet or the innkeeper Benois been picked up
and subjected to torture by the Gestapo, they could
honestly say that they knew Pierre Touchette as a
dim-witted garage helper.

In the beginning George was afraid that a crisis
might shock him out of his assumed role, but as
time went on he realized that it had grown around
him so tightly that no circumstances could ever
cause it to be penetrated.

Curfew was at nine o'clock. One night George,
mistaking the time, passed two German guards
close to a bridge over one of the many canals which
criss-crossed the district. They asked for his pass
and then one of them recognized him. "It's that idiot
from the garage," he said in disgust. "Don't bother
him; he probably can't tell the time." This was a
triumph which George hugged to himself. The
small incident gave him confidence that he would
never make a slip that would reveal his true identity. If he was accepted by military guards, he would
be accepted by anyone.

The escape route was well organized now, and
with increased British air activity more and more
customers were appearing before the Torigni troop.
The success of the Rat Run depended in part upon
the briefing given to airmen before they took off

from their English bases. The rules for escape and contact with Resistance men were worked out by London and passed on by radio to the various Resistance troops. One week, for instance, airmen who would be bombing Saint-Lô or other targets in the Torigni area (or who might be shot down passing over the area en route to Berlin or Hamburg) would be given specific orders as the rules for the week.

"When you land, move fast to get out of the neighborhood," they were told. "Then bury your 'chute. The area is filled with hedges. Find one and hide yourself until ten o'clock the next morning. Your flying boots are so built that you can cut the upper part of them off. Do this immediately. Now the bottom parts of your boots will look like ordinary peasant shoes. Turn your tunics inside out and bury your helmet. At ten A.M. walk to the nearest road. Remember, the crash of your plane by now will be known to every Resistance man in the area, and they'll be out looking for you. How will you know them? You won't, but they'll know you. When you hit a road, face north and then sit down on what will then be the left side of the road. If the road runs east-west, face west and then sit down on the left side of the roadway. If you see anyone approaching, bend over and appear to be tying your shoe laces. If the man, woman or child approaching says "Follow me" in English, you will know that here is your contact. It may be a senile man, a ten-year-old child, a priest or a nun. No matter who it is, you follow and obey orders." If the airmen fell farther inland from Torigni, they were led to Thibaut's farm by messengers from villages close to the scene of the parachuting. If they fell in the district (and because the aircraft fire protecting Saint-Lô was so intense, many did drop in the area) they were picked up on the road by members of the troop or by youngsters on bicycles who had orders to speak only to men sitting on the left side of the road tying shoe laces.

Usually after a British plane had crashed, the Germans made an intensive search for airmen who had parachuted to safety. Men picked up by the Torigni troop were kept at the farm until the search had been given up. Then they were led across fields to a farm just outside Saint-Lô. The responsibility was now that of the highly organized Saint-Lô Resistance men, who also had British agents helping them.

If the weather was propitious, the airmen were put into fishing boats which would slip out at night for rendezvous with the fast British rescue launches which often came to within four or five miles of the French shore. If the weather was not right, or if the Germans' vigilance was such that the sea route seemed too risky, the airmen were moved south across the Spanish border and sent to Gibraltar.

One night an especially attractive young fighter pilot was picked up. George stood by as the priest began to question him. Had he been shot down by flak? "That's for sure," the pilot laughed. Was he in a hurry to get back? "That's for sure," the youngster repeated. And George's heart missed a beat. He recognized the slang and the accent of Western Canada. Back in Winnipeg and Edmonton and Calgary he'd heard the expression "That's for sure" a thousand times. This lad was obviously a Canadian from his own part of the West, but he could only stand there, his lower lip hanging foolishly, while every impulse was to throw his arms around the pilot's shoulders and ask him how things were back home. It was one of the very few times that the personality of George DuPre struggled momentarily for recognition. But it was only a flicker, and then George DuPre dropped back into the subconscious mind of Pierre Touchette. He was, in some ways, three men, the least of whom was Du-Pre. The second man was the well-trained, nameless agent who thought, never felt, a machine obeying orders from London. Then there was the outward personality of Pierre Touchette, whose mannerisms and speech were the automatic expressions of the idiot.

Pierre Touchette now was as much a part of the village as the real Pierre Touchette would have been. Everyone liked the amiable, grinning half-

wit. Even the kicks he received from Gestapo officers were only half-hearted kicks; their kicks were
in the nature of good-natured slaps at an affection-
ate dog. Regular German army officers never kicked
him at all. They were meticulous in observing the
traditions of their service. They had small liking
for this business of occupation. This, they felt, was
Gestapo work. They often talked freely in front of
the village half-wit; he heard them express their
contempt for the Gestapo dozens of times. They
called them "the scum"; they regarded them as
misfits whose physical or mental infirmities pre-
vented them from joining the regular army.

More than seventy airmen had passed through
Torigni by now. New orders began to come from
London. The time for more active resistance had
come. Dynamite, fuses, hand grenades were dropped now and buried to await the day when orders
would call for their use. The orders were not long
in coming. George was ordered to blow up a control tower in the Saint-Lô yards.

In France these railroad installations were called
"signal boxes." The one which had been assigned
to George was a large one controlling all traffic
entering the large Saint-Lô freight yards. Dozens of
switches were controlled by this one tower, and if
it could be destroyed it would tangle all freight
traffic for two or three days. George had learned
that destroying tracks was hardly worth the ex-

penditure of valuable dynamite. The Germans were efficient in replacing torn and twisted rails within an hour after they had been blown up. But if you destroyed a control tower you destroyed the electrical equipment which controlled the switches, and these were difficult to replace and put in operation again. Ammunition for the Saint-Lô anti-aircraft was channeled into the city via the tracks controlled by the tower, and if it could be put out of commission it would delay delivery of the ammo and limit the usefulness of Saint-Lô's aerial defenses.

George had been given a bicycle by Lavelle. He biked to Saint-Lô to look the situation over. He found that the German guards protecting the freight yards were stationed about a hundred yards apart. The defense was general, with no special guards assigned to the control tower. The next night was a dark one and George took off alone, with six sticks of dynamite and a fuse concealed in the tool bag of his bike. He skirted the two military checkposts on the road by dragging his bike into the fields. Half a mile from the freight yards he hid his wheel, removed the dynamite and fuse and walked slowly through the dark night. The guards, complacent because no sabotage had been attempted here and because the moonless night would probably keep the RAF bombers at home, weren't as alert as they might have been. George managed to penetrate the outer cordon easily enough, and then he crawled the remaining hundred yards toward the tower. It was built on heavy stilts, and it was easy to tie the sticks together and then fasten the bundle of explosive to one of the supports. The only ticklish moment came when he lit the fuse. This was the old-fashioned, primitive method of using dynamite, but it was considered the best way to deal with small installations. George lit the fuse and melted into the darkness. He knew that the slow burning, six-foot fuse wouldn't reach the explosive for half an hour, by which time he hoped to be back in his own bailiwick. There was a persistent rain and not a trace of a moon; it was like bicycling through black coffee, George felt. Just before he reached the garage the night was split by a sharp explosion, and George knew that his mission had been successful.

A second series of explosions followed the sound of the first, and he saw the sky above Saint-Lô bisected with red and golden streaks. This puzzled him until the next morning, when the priest, who had been informed by the Saint-Lô troop, said that a string of box cars loaded with ammunition had caught fire when George's six sticks had made a burning pyre out of the control tower. The news was sent to London, and that night the RAF bombers came over in force and relative safety; the ack-ack fire was weak and ineffective.

The problem of how much dynamite to use or

whether a grenade might be more efficacious, how to locate the weak point of doomed installation, presented no real difficulty; George had been thoroughly schooled in this technique at Oxford. The only real problem was the transporting of the explosives to the desired location. It was immediate death for anyone found with a weapon or explosives in his possession. And he needed help to transport the explosives this time. The priest resolved this difficulty.

"Madame Bouvot will oblige," he smiled. "She has been waiting for such an opportunity."

"Madame Bouvot?" George was puzzled.

"You recall those enormous skirts she wears? She could hide a dozen grenades beneath one of those voluminous affairs. They could be attached to —well . . . to whatever it is that women wear under their skirts."

A few days later George received orders to destroy a large shed which stood in the center of a truck-repair installation, seven miles from the village. The shed held spare parts to replenish all the German trucks in the area. He took Madame Bouvot with him this time. She concealed six sticks of explosive under her skirt while George put six more in his tool bag. The truck installation covered a three-acre field. At least sixty trucks were there ready to be serviced the next morning. The half-wit garage helper and the plump, sixty-year-old woman bicycled silently but companionably through the night. George had a feeling of real affection for this incredibly courageous woman, but he couldn't convey it to her without discarding his assumed role. George stopped half a mile from the field and slid from his bike. Wordlessly the widow followed suit. The priest had told her to obey the garage helper on this operation, but when George asked her for the dynamite she carried he noticed that she hesitated. He suddenly realized why, and walked a few paces from her and turned his back. He heard the rustling of a skirt and then a whispered, "Here, boy . . . Good luck." He carried his bicycle bag with six sticks and stuffed the six she had given him inside his shirt. He told her to go home and she nodded.

He walked to within a hundred yards of the hedge which framed the field. He lay under the hedge waiting for the guard to pass. He lay there half an hour noticing that the guard patroled this point every ten minutes. When he was sure that this was the routine he slipped through the hedge after the German had walked by and crawled to the relative safety of the parked trucks. He crawled under them, working his way to the center of the installation. He reached the large shed and was gratified to notice a row of gasoline cans parked neatly outside. He hurriedly arranged the sticks, attached them to the building and then affixed the fuse. He lit it and began crawling back to the hedge.

He lay inside the field until he heard the steps of the methodical guard. He knew he'd have ten minutes to crawl to the hedge, wedge his way through it to the relative safety of the road. It took him less than ten minutes to reach his bicycle.

He had traveled only three miles when he heard the explosion. He looked back and saw a bright flash in the sky and then a dull and sustained red glow. The spare parts had most certainly been destroyed; the fire lit by the gasoline was giving him a dividend in the form of dozens of blazing trucks. He hurried home just in time to escape the military cars which thundered through the village on their way to investigate the blaze.

The underground had a reliable grapevine which functioned speedily. Twelve hours later George learned that every truck repair installation for a hundred miles around had been sabotaged on the same night. The trucks were vitally important to the Germans; the mobile anti-aircraft guns and the huge searchlights were transported by trucks. With hundreds of trucks knocked out of commission on the same night, the RAF bombers had an easy week of it, and they blasted Saint-Lô and every other important target in the area furiously without too much trouble from the flak.

Within a few months the life of the village and the movements of both military and Gestapo had resolved themselves into a predictable pattern.

Once this pattern was clear in his mind, he knew that anything that seemed to contradict it or did not follow the pattern exactly was out of the ordinary. One day he was bicycling along a road which led to Saint-Lô. The road bent sharply and he noticed that a dozen Germans were chopping down the trees that bordered the road on the inside of the bend. Why were they doing this? It wasn't for firewood, for they merely dragged the trees into the brush and left them there. He visited the bend a week later. Some twenty feet of trees and brush had been cleared, but only here at the bend in the road. This, he noticed, had the effect of widening the road at the bend. It made a sweeping turn instead of a sharp one. Was it to make the road more accessible for heavy tanks? That didn't seem reasonable; the tanks could have negotiated the sharp turns easily enough.

"If you ever notice anything out of the ordinary, report it to us," Baker had said again and again. "It may seem trivial; it may be trivial. Report it anyway."

On a third visit he noticed something else. Just before he reached the bend he saw that a path had been cleared from the road to a large barn a hundred yards off the road. It was a wide path, wide enough to permit a large truck to turn off the road and reach the barn. In itself this was a trivial incident. But George wasn't sure. A week later he bicycled along another road leading to the coast. He was startled to see Germans again clearing away underbrush and trees at a bend. Bicycling back he saw that a path had been cleared to a barn, just as in the first incident. He couldn't ignore these puzzling facts which didn't fit into the accepted pattern. That night he wrote out a long coded report, explaining what he had seen; he felt a little foolish when he asked the priest to send it, but he recalled Baker's words, "Report anything out of the ordinary." An answer came quickly from London. "Give us exact location road bends and barns." He radioed the information.

The next day a Spitfire streaked low over the area. Germans seldom went up after a lone plane. This one flew so low and so fast that ack-ack couldn't reach it. George wondered if there was any connection between his report and the flight of the Spitfire over the area which included the two barns. This Spit might, he felt, be a photographic plane. Two days later he discovered that there was a definite connection between his report and the visit of the Spitfire. Four light, fast bomber fighters dropped from the sky one clear afternoon. They zoomed low over the village, continued on a mile and dropped their bombs. They swerved west another mile and dropped more bombs. The next day while filling up the gas tank of a Gestapo car, he heard the officers joking about the RAF bombers which had visited the district.

"They hit nothing but two old barns," one laughed. "Just makes no sense."

It didn't make much sense to George either until a few days later, when he received a message from London telling him to keep his eyes out for any further clearing of road bends. London explained that heavy invasion barges were being concentrated behind the coast. They were hidden in barns, and when the time came they would be put on trucks and driven to the ports. They were too wide to negotiate the hairpin turns of some country roads unless the trees were removed to give them clearance. London added that all agents and Resistance men had been alerted to look for road bends which had been widened and for barns to which recently cleared paths had been cut. Apparently the Gestapo wasn't aware of the concentration of barges; the military seldom took the Gestapo into its confidence.

During the following weeks the priest received reports that dozens of barns hiding invasion barges had been spotted in other areas and had been subsequently destroyed. The invasion never came off. George never knew whether the discovery of the barns had been a factor in the decision of the German General Staff not to launch an attack on England. But he did know that he'd never again hesitate to report any slightest deviation from the normal activities of the Germans.

During the following months sabotage increased. Every week crates of dynamite framed by two feet of rubber sponge were dropped and cached away in haylofts, the most reliable of all hideaways. RAF fighter-bombers came over every day now strafing roads and then bombing the railroad bridges. Bombs were more effective against the heavily constructed and heavily guarded railroad bridges than dynamite would have been. The bridges over the canals, however, were given to George as targets. He blew up a dozen of these, another dozen control towers and several viaducts. He never went on an operation without first carefully surveying the target and the method of guarding it.

By now he was familiar with the car and license plates of the leading military and Gestapo officials in the area. He knew that Colonel Herman Hinkel, the local military commander, spent every Tuesday and Thursday night with a comely French girl whose morals and patriotism were quite elastic. He knew it and the men commanded by the Colonel knew it. On Tuesdays and Thursdays the majors and captains took things easy; they knew their chief wouldn't be around on any inspection tours as long as the charms of the French girl held him. Their men, knowing that the officers weren't around much on Tuesdays or Thursdays, relaxed too.

It was on these nights that George did most of his sabotage. It was seldom that he had narrow escapes. The thick hedges of Normandy were his great protection. On a dark night—and George seldom went on sabotage missions when the moon was full—a sentry would have to step on you before he knew you were there. Both military and Gestapo leaders, furious over the increased sabotage in the area, finally tightened up all regulations and made increasingly careful searches. They had searched the garage and George's lean-to a dozen times, but they seldom gave the idiot helper more than an impatient boot out of the way. Quite often they would round up a dozen men and women, take them to headquarters, search them and let them go. George and the priest were more careful than ever about whom they allowed to transport the dynamite. They trusted the calm efficiency of Madame Bouvot more than anyone else, and George used her almost exclusively. If she realized that George was more than the jibbering idiot he seemed, she never hinted at her knowledge. She regarded George with good-humored affection. Occasionally he caught her looking at him with speculative interest but when he caught her gaze she would look away.

"Somewhere you learned to handle explosives very well," she said one night.

"My father taught me," he mumbled.

"I knew your father," she said dryly. "He

couldn't light his pipe without burning the rug."

"He taught me," George insisted.

"All right, Pierre," she said softly, "if you say so. But be careful. We don't want you to get hurt."

One afternoon the Gestapo drew up in front of the post office and herded everyone who happened to be on the streets into their truck. Madame Bouvot was one of those caught at her early morning marketing. But neither the priest nor George worried. They had absolutely no reason to suspect her. They would merely search her and then, finding nothing, would release her as they had released everyone else after these quick raids. It didn't quite work out that way. They heard the story next day. Madame Bouvot had objected to being searched by these pigs of Gestapo men and her violent tongue and indignant expressions of contempt had actually overawed them. She was an old woman, she stormed, respected in the community by Germans as well as French. She demanded to be taken to Saint-Lô Gestapo headquarters. She knew the Colonel in charge, she said, and if he insisted that she submit to the indignity of a search, she would agree to it. The sergeant in charge of the raid was bewildered at the unexpected opposition. He couldn't beat this old woman into submission. And suppose —just suppose—she was a friend of the Colonel? He decided to play it safe. He took her to Saint-Lô headquarters and told the story. It reached the Colo-

nel in charge. He had never heard of Madame Bouvot. He stormed angrily into the interrogation room
to confront her. Four of his officers followed him.

"You insist that I remove my clothes and be
searched," she demanded.

"I certainly do," he bellowed.

"In that case I will help you," she said calmly
lifting up the folds of her voluminous skirts. She
lifted the skirt and reached for something which
hung from her corset by a hook. They never saw
what it was; she pulled the pin and the hand grenade she had concealed there exploded, blowing
everyone in the room to bits.

It was Doctor Rennet who told the priest why the
old woman had destroyed herself. Her heart was in
very bad condition, the doctor said. He, the doctor,
had warned her that she'd have to stop her underground activities. She couldn't stand even the physical strain of carrying six sticks of dynamite.

"I'm actually in danger of dying from this heart
condition?" she demanded. The doctor, knowing
that this sturdy, self-reliant woman would not be
put off with evasions or lies, had reluctantly admitted that that was true. "Well," she had said
calmly, "if I am to die I will take some of these
swine with me." Apparently she had been carrying
the grenade around for some time, hoping that a
chance would come to destroy some high-ranking

members of the Gestapo. When the chance came she took advantage of it. There were many prayers said in Père Gauraud's little church the next morning for the repose of the soul of the valiant Madame Bouvot.

CHAPTER VII

Occasionally one of the troop stole a German car when an operation was to be carried out too far away for bicycling. Because George had so pinpointed the nocturnal habits of certain officers, the theft of a car was fairly simple. If a German car parked outside a farmhouse every Tuesday night always remained there until seven A.M., it was a good bet that the German officer inside the house would never miss the vehicle until that time. Three or four of the men of the troop would push the car away from the farmhouse and then, with the use of one of the many ignition keys clever Georges Lavelle had fashioned, would start it up. If they stuck to back roads the car was never stopped. If challenged, the driver would yell in German, "Gestapo officers, you pigs," and the startled sentry would invariably draw back.

It was Farmer Thibaut who suggested another use for stolen German cars. The constant diet of horse meat was particularly annoying to the farmer, who had to care for twenty-six fine beef cattle. These had once been owned by him; now he merely took care of them for the benefit of the Germans. Not a cow, not even a chicken, could be killed and eaten. Each one was registered by the Germans, and when needed was requisitioned. Thibaut stole a German car one night. He drove it along the road adjacent to his farm. He and burly Albert Baudouin had pole-axed one of his steers earlier that evening. Now they dragged the carcass to the middle of the road. They ran the German car over the body of the steer, drove the car back to where they had originally found it, and then Farmer Thibaut reported to the police that one of his cows had been hit and killed by a car driven by a German officer. The gendarmes immediately reported this to the German military post two miles outside the village. Four men led by a lieutenant appeared at Thibaut's farm at daylight. The methodical lieutenant examined the body of the cow thoroughly.

"Ah," he exclaimed triumphantly. "Tire tracks on the hide."

He peered at the tracks and nodded in satisfaction. "You were right," he said. "It was a Gestapo car, driven by a high ranking officer. You see their marks? These tires were oversize. These marks came from new tires. Only the Gestapo gets new tires," he added bitterly.

"Will you take the body of the cow away?" Thibaut said. "It is of course no good to anyone. This cow has been dead for at least ten hours, and the meat is poisoned by now."

"Bury the damn cow yourself," the army officer said irritably.

Fifteen minutes later Thibaut and Benois were butchering the steer and hanging the meat in the farmer's ancient ice house. For a week the eight members of the Resistance movement and George DuPre feasted upon steaks, chops, and roast beef. Even without such windfalls George never went hungry. The monotony of his horse-meat and black-bread diet was occasionally relieved by the appearance of fresh eggs, cheese, butter and milk left outside his shack during the early morning hours. He never knew where the food came from, and he asked no questions.

Le Chien Noir was the gathering place for the men of the district when they'd finished their daily chores. George would slip unobtrusively into the café, sit in an obscure corner and listen. If members of the troop happened to be there they'd give the garage helper a casual greeting but never identify themselves with him. Occasionally a German car would stop outside and two or three Gestapo officers would come into Le Chien Noir. Gerard Benois would always treat them pleasantly; the priest had impressed upon his little band the necessity of maintaining the outward show of amiability toward the Germans. More than once an officer, seeing Pierre Touchette sitting in the corner, would remember that he was the slow-witted chap who filled his car with petrol at the local garage and he'd toss a careless *"Donnez à ce pauvre fou un verre a boir"* to the café owner, and genial Benois would "give the poor fool a drink" of Framboise, Mirabelle or Calvados, all of which were made locally. George had always been virtually a teetotaler for the simple reason that he didn't like the taste of alcohol. He really suffered as he sipped the raw fiery spirits and yearned for a Coca-Cola.

It wasn't long before George learned those who must at all costs be avoided, those with whom tongues had to be especially closely guarded. He learned that the most dangerous Frenchmen of all were those employed by the railroads or those who were civil servants. Most of these men were middle-aged or elderly, and all looked forward to the pension toward which they'd been working so many years. The Germans, through the Laval government, had made it plain that all seniority rights would be respected if government and railroad workers toed the line. If a track or a bridge was destroyed near a railroad station, the station master would receive the blame; he should be on the alert against sabotage. If postal employees, municipal workers or others on the government payroll did not report any Resistance activity they knew of, things would go badly with them; their rights to a pension would be immediately cut off. They would talk freely in the café, and Gerard Benois behind the bar and Pierre Touchette sitting in the corner would listen carefully. George came to the conclusion that you could never trust a French civil-service employee; these men had too much at stake. A frown from the Gestapo and they were off the pension lists. If, on the other hand, they reported Resistance activities, they were marked for promotion and perhaps earlier retirement. The confidence of the Germans in the early months of 1942 was supreme, and, George had to admit, well founded. The Luftwaffe had stepped up the air raids against England. The Resistance men listened surreptitiously to the BBC broadcasts and believed them, but the ordinary uneasy, security-minded civil service or railway worker neither listened nor believed reports of Britain's strong defensive fight. To them the war was about over, and anyone who did not accept the fact of German victory was a fool.

George was finding out that the word "patriotism" had many meanings. Listening night after night not only to the casual visitors to the café but

to his eight colleagues, he realized that each man
had his own particular reasons for either fighting
the Germans or collaborating with them. The station master would say quite frankly that he accepted Laval's estimate of the situation; the war was
lost and France could survive only by co-operating
with her German masters. Those who fought on,
like his eight colleagues, did it for various reasons,
the least of which was love of France. Madame Bouvot's husband had been killed in the First World
War, her son had been killed early in this one—she
had fought to avenge them. The little priest felt
that Hitler had set himself up as an anti-Christ. He
fought to wipe out the sacrilege Hitler had committed. He didn't fight for France, he fought for his
Church and his God. Farmer Thibaut fought for his
farm. This had been his life. Now the Germans had
taken his chickens, his live stock, his vegetables,
and until they were driven out of the land he could
never call the farm his own. Big Albert Baudouin
had no family. He didn't hate the Germans especially; he didn't love France especially. To him the
blowing up of bridges and trains, aiding downed
airmen to escape, was all part of a glorious adventure, an escape from the every-day routine of ham-
mering iron into curved horseshoes. Old Doctor
Rennet had a warm love for the neighbors, so many
of whom he had brought into the world. France?
To him the concept of dying for one's country was

too abstract to grasp; to risk one's life for the people of his village—that was something else again. None of the eight could be called a patriot, George felt, in the sense that the young British pilots were patriots. These youngsters were fighting to preserve their country, their way of life, and they weren't ashamed of admitting it. They were all desperately anxious to return to England so they could get back to fighting. Frenchmen in the village of Torigni never talked of their country. And yet George knew that his eight co-workers would die rather than reveal the secret of each other's identity. They were tremendously loyal to one another and to the dim-witted Pierre Touchette.

Finally George met a French patriot. He was fourteen, and he bore the unlikely name of Armand Owens. Armand's father had been a British soldier who had fought in Normandy during the First World War. He had met a pretty French girl in a village not far from Torigni. The war over, Trooper Owens returned to England, but he couldn't get the memory of the French girl out of his mind. So he returned to Normandy, wooed her and married her. It wasn't until 1928 that young Armand was born. Owens lived in France now, but he had the intense love for the country of his birth most Englishmen have for their country, and he communicated his intense devotion to his son. But he taught his boy to remember always that he was a French citizen first; his primary love should be for his own country, and then if he had love to spare, perhaps he might give it to England. The father had died in 1939 of pneumonia, but his tough English spirit lived again in this boy. The boy's mother was a skilled seamstress who worked in Saint-Lô. They needed no children for the Saint-Lô Resistance movement, but young Armand had heard of the four girls who had been shot for delivering messages for the underground fighters, and he wanted to be part of the war against the Germans. His mother's brother owned a farm outside of Torigni, and he went there ostensibly to work for him on the land. But within a few weeks he had become one of George's messengers. He was a small but sturdy lad, quick-witted and strong-legged. Gradually he was given increasingly important jobs to do. He had located a German ammunition dump only five miles away, and one night he returned to the village laden down with grenades which he had stolen. The priest told him angrily never to do anything like this again. If he wanted to be one of them, the first thing he had to learn was to obey orders and never institute any independent action.

"Then give me orders, Père Gauraud," the boy said simply.

"I will send you orders through Pierre Touchette. You know *le pauvre fou* Pierre?" The boy nodded. "Every Monday and Wednesday night you report to him in the shack where he lives. If I have any orders, he will tell you."

Bad weather had forced the cancellation of two drops, and the shortage of dynamite had brought sabotage activities to a temporary halt. Twice the boy Armand reported to Pierre Touchette, but there were no orders for him. He remained to talk with the man he apparently knew only as the village half-wit, and George encouraged him to talk. Armand told of his English father. He talked of his love for both England and France, and George glowed inwardly. This might have been an English lad. Neither excitement nor sheer hatred of Germans drove this boy; he was impelled only by his honest patriotism.

Armand thought of the ammunition dump as his own particular discovery. His uncle grew very fine cabbages, which gave the boy an idea. One morning he gathered six large, beautiful heads of cabbage and headed for the German camp. When the sentry stopped him he showed him the cabbages, winked, and said in bad but understandable German, "I stole these from my uncle's farm for your cook. Your cook is my friend. Let me in to see him." The sentry was delighted. It wasn't often that these French swine showed any signs of voluntary co-operation. And some fresh cabbages would certainly add something to the monotony of the German army rations. A small army detachment had the duty of guarding this ammo dump. It was a drab, dull duty. They had to live here and eat here, and they had no transport to visit even the little village of Torigni or the larger town of Saint-Lô, only fifteen miles away. There certainly could be no harm in letting this child, who carried nothing more dangerous than cabbages, through the gate.

Armand walked into the large field which contained the stacked boxes of dynamite, grenades and ammunition all shielded from the rain by open sheds.The camp was guarded on three sides by heavy barbed wire; a strong hedge framed the fourth side. The boy saw smoke rising from the chimney of a low, prefabricated building, and he reasoned quite correctly that this was the kitchen. He walked toward it confidently and entered the building and in a loud voice asked for the cook. The fattest man Armand had ever seen looked up from his stove and said that he was the cook. Armand, with a shy grin, handed him the six beautiful cabbages. The cook had an assistant from Alsace-Lorraine, and the assistant, noting the boy's stumbling German, came to his rescue in French. Eager lies poured forth from Armand's lips. He hated his uncle who made him work hard in the fields all day and who beat him and fed him nothing but black bread and horse meat. All of his chickens and pigs and vegetables went to the Gestapo. He had made some deal with them, Armand said, so that they got everything. The cook nodded grimly. It was true that the Gestapo did get the best of everything. They had no strict army budget; they didn't have to live on army rations.

"If I stole cabbages and tomatoes from my uncle's farm and brought them to you," Armand said, "maybe you would sometimes give me a piece of chocolate."

The cook roared with laughter. "You can have all the chocolate you want. Just bring us fresh vegetables."

Armand soon became a familiar figure in the camp. It wasn't long before he had picked up enough German to understand the labels on the precious boxes of explosives. Now he told the priest what he had done. Père Gauraud was torn between admiration for the boy's ingenuity and worry over the possibility that he might be discovered.

"But what have I done?" Armand asked innocently. "I have only stolen a few vegetables from my uncle, and he really doesn't care. And by now I know where they keep everything: dynamite, cordite, everything." His eyes were dancing with anticipation.

"We don't need anything right now," the priest told him, "so just take it easy and report to Pierre regularly."

Armand just wouldn't take it easy. Every morning he'd go to the camp with a few stolen vegetables. He became such a familiar figure that he was hardly noticed even when he wandered into the sheds which contained the explosives. The cook had been in a bad temper one morning; he had been ordered to prepare a good meal for a group of high-ranking visitors. There would be fifteen of them, he'd stormed. "I'd like to put cordite in their soup."

"Would that make the soup explode?" Armand asked, puzzled.

The French-speaking Alsatian chuckled and explained to Armand the peculiar properties of cordite. Mingled with other elements it was an explosive; by itself it was no more dangerous than castor oil. It was, in fact, the assistant cook laughed, the strongest laxative known; too powerful even to give to horses. Now those words came back to Armand as he strolled through the shed. The sleepy sentry sitting on a barrel that held dynamite saw nothing but a wide-eyed boy munching on a chocolate bar. This was the boy who brought the fresh vegetables to the mess, he recalled. He dozed off, unconscious of the fact that the boy was searching for a box or a barrel labeled cordite. Armand found it at the far end of the shed. The cover of the box was loose; it took him half a minute to pry it open, thrust his small hand into the box and emerge with a fistful of the white powder called cordite. He shoved it into his pocket and then grabbed another handful.

"*Was machts du dort?*" the sentry called.

"*Rien, rien,*" Armand said casually, walking toward him.

"You stick to the kitchen," the sentry growled half-heartedly. "Stay out of here."

Armand went back to the kitchen. A huge tureen of soup was heating on the stove. The cook was at the end of the kitchen instructing his assistant in the proper way to season a pie. Armand reached into his pocket and emptied the cordite into the tureen. Now he would let nature take its course.

The next morning he was back at the camp with an armful of vegetables, but the sentry refused to allow him to enter the gate.

"I'll tell my friend the cook," Armand protested stoutly.

"Your friend the cook is in jail," the sentry growled. "Someone poisoned the food last night. Fifteen officers were stricken. Three of them had to be taken to the hospital."

"Poison in the food?"

"Yes," the sentry said. "They all ate their soup, and then one by one they started making dashes for the latrines. It was very funny to see them run. But then two of them collapsed; it wasn't funny then. The soup was poisoned, all right, and they took it away to be analyzed. They'll soon know what was in it. No one thinks the cook did it, but someone sneaked into the kitchen, all right, and the cook is responsible."

Armand left. He couldn't keep this colossal joke to himself. He had to tell someone. He didn't think the little priest would laugh at what he had done. Perhaps Pierre Touchette would appreciate it. That night he hurried to George's shack. He found the village half-wit reading a book, and when Armand saw the nature of the book he forgot all about the joke he had played on the Germans.

George was lying on his cot reading a Bible printed in English. George had found it in the home of the blacksmith some weeks previously. It had been there since the first war when a group of British Tommies had been billeted in the black-smith's home. One of them had left the Bible behind when orders came to move forward. George had seen it and had surreptitiously removed it. He'd wondered at that time whether a black mark would be placed against him for stealing a Bible. He consoled himself with the thought that Albert Baudouin would gladly have given him the book had he asked for it, but he didn't want the black-smith to know that he spoke English. Only four of the troop knew that he was British; the others might have guessed by now, but they couldn't be sure, and the fewer who were sure, the less the risk of exposure. And so he had taken the Bible, and it had comforted him on lonely nights and he felt, too, that it gave him added strength.

The boy walked over to his cot, looked in amazement at the Bible and said scornfully in English, "I never heard of a spy reading the Bible."

George was shocked speechless. No one had addressed him in English since his arrival a year and a half ago. This fourteen-year-old lad apparently had guessed that he was English. If he knew, how many others had penetrated his disguise? He looked steadily at young Armand Owens.

"Don't worry, Pierre," the youngster laughed. "I won't tell anyone."

"Who told you?" George asked in the voice of George DuPre, but to his amazement the words came out in the slurred accents of Pierre Touchette.

"No one, Pierre," the boy said. "But I knew. You forget that I'm half English. You can fool the Boches and the others in the village, but you can't fool me. My father was an English soldier. I knew Père Gauraud couldn't blow up bridges; neither could old Madame Bouvot. What do they know about dynamite? So I guessed it was you. You don't think I'd ever tell anyone, Pierre. Not even the Gestapo, not if they set me on fire. I wouldn't tell . . ."

"I believe you, Armand," George said slowly. "But never mind that. You think it odd that I read the Bible?"

"Sure it's odd. That's for kids, not for spies."

"You're wrong, you know," George told him. "Kid's don't need the Bible as much as grown-ups do. Even spies need the Bible; especially spies need the Bible, Armand. Let me tell you some of the stories from the Bible."

"Even the names in the Bible don't sound right," the boy frowned. "Whoever heard of people named Jesus and those others?"

"Well, let's give them new names—English names," George said. "Let's call God, 'Tom' and Jesus, 'Harry.' Let me tell you how Harry died for us . . ."

The boy came nearly every night after that to listen to stories from the Bible. He liked the idea of calling God "Tom." He could understand the Almighty better if you gave him a down-to-earth English name. George found that these talks with the youngster did him good. He hadn't realized it, but he had missed the ordinary human relationship with his fellows. For a year and a half he had been playing a part; he could relax with the boy and articulate some of his hopes, and talk of his wife in Canada, and he could arouse the boy's interest with his tales of the Arctic. But most of all he tried to teach the boy the meaning of faith. And one night he realized that he was succeeding.

Orders came from London. A railroad switch

some six miles away was to be destroyed immediately. George surveyed the site and realized that he
would need twice as much explosive as he had on
hand. He decided to let young Armand guide him
while he stole the dynamite from the German ammunition dump. The youngster was proud to be
given the assignment. By now Armand knew the
habits of every sentry who guarded the hedge. He
told George that one of them was fairly old. When
he walked his assigned portion of the hedge he only
gave cursory attention to it. He walked rapidly, and
then at the end of his tour he would smoke a cigarette, warm himself, and then resume his monot-
onous and solitary duty. George and the boy could
slip through the hedge which he guarded; they
would have little trouble locating the explosive, nor
would it be difficult to carry it to the hedge. They
would lie there under the hedge while the old sentry made his hurried tour, and then when he had
passed they could get away easily enough. Everything went according to schedule at first. They
slipped through the hedge as planned. The quick,
sure eyes of the boy saw a case labeled explosive;
together they lifted it and brought it to the hedge.
They shoved the box beneath the hedge and then
far to the right they heard the footsteps of the
sentry. There was a bright moon that night. George
saw the sentry advancing and he froze. This wasn't
the inefficient, weary old man; this was a bright,

alert sentry whom Armand had told him of, and whom George had decided to avoid at all costs. George heard the youngster's startled gasp. Then he felt the boy's hand tighten on his arm and he heard his whisper, "Don't worry, Pierre—Tom is with us." George lay close to the earth praying that the beam of the sentry's flashlight would not reveal the huddled shapes of himself and the boy. The sentry passed within twelve feet of where they lay. The sentry, who usually scanned every foot of the hedge, for once was careless. When his footsteps receded George and the boy crawled slowly, noiselessly away. An hour later they were back in the shack behind the garage.

"Tom was with us, wasn't he?" the boy asked with strange insistence.

"He sure was, Armand," George said somberly. "We didn't do this job alone. Some day, Armand, you'll grow up a little more and then you won't be afraid to call God by his proper name."

"Maybe," the boy said a little shyly.

The railroad switch presented no problem the next night. Its destruction did, however, have the effect of tightening the German grip on the village. A group of Gestapo men stormed into Torigni to search every home, every shop, every barn. But not a stick of dynamite nor a single grenade was found.

Four British airmen chose this unpropitious moment to bail out near the village, and they were hurried to Farmer Thibaut's farm. Two of them revealed themselves as Pathfinders. These were especially trained men who flew to a target ahead of the bombing formations. Expert at navigation, it was they who located the targets and dropped flares to illuminate them. Their efficient work had increased the effectiveness of night-time bombing tremendously, and London had ordered George to take extra care of these pilots and navigators. Quite definitely they were not expendable, and they knew too much to be allowed to fall into German hands. The Germans were now using pentathol, the "truth serum," with considerable success; it unloosened the tongue of some of the most stubborn RAF pilots. It was not infallible, but it was causing grave concern to the RAF brass. George didn't like the idea of leaving the two Pathfinders in Thibaut's farm. The little priest came up with an answer to the problem.

"We have a convent some six miles from here," he told George. "I haven't mentioned it before because I hated the thought of exposing the nuns to danger. But they are all loyal Frenchwomen, and the Mother Superior has told me that she is anxious to help. I suggest we move the two Pathfinder lads to the convent and keep them there until things quiet down."

George agreed, and the two young pilots were hurried to the convent, where they donned the black dresses and white headdress of the order. They remained there ten days and were then moved farther along the Rat Run.

Now for the first time American pilots and crewmen began to appear. As usual, the priest questioned them with George acting as a silent witness. The Americans hadn't been given the same briefing which made the RAF pilots so tractable. They were annoyed at the interrogation by the little priest, and were obviously disgusted at the presence of the unwashed, drooling half-wit in the oil-soaked clothes.

"Let's brush these two characters off and start off on our own," one pilot said, loud enough for George to hear. "If we have to depend on a padre and an idiot, we're done for."

George whispered in the priest's ear, and then Père Gauraud gave the two a little lecture. "We've managed to save about a hundred RAF airmen in the past two years," he said dryly. "Perhaps you'd better trust us. We have already informed London that you are here. We've been at this for a long time, lads. We may seem over-cautious, but if one of you is picked up and is made to talk, it could mean that never again will an airman shot down in this area be sent back to England. We're moving you on tonight to a farm three miles from here. Pierre will guide you there."

"For God's sake," one of them exploded. *"Him?"*

The priest nodded and a little smile touched the corner of his mouth. "Yes, him. Obey him implicitly."

"We got to trust a half-wit?" one of them mumbled.

"The half-wit has saved the lives of a great many airmen." The little priest was angry enough to give the two Americans a hint as to who the half-wit really was, but George pressed his shoulder sharply and the anger went out of him.

"Just follow him," the priest said coldly. "If he stops, you stop. If he bends down to pick a flower, you fall flat on your faces and lie still. If you are accosted by anyone, let him do the talking."

They shook their heads doubtfully, but followed George into the night. He cut across fields, stopping every few moments to listen. Once he heard sounds of laughter, and he reached down to pluck a flower. The two Americans fell to the ground. The laughter came from the home of a comely widow, and George knew that she was entertaining Oberst Franz Genthner of the Gestapo. He led the men on to the farmhouse, which was the next port of call on the Rat Run. One of the Americans looked curiously at Pierre.

"I've got a hunch that you aren't as dumb as you make out," he said.

Pierre grinned foolishly, and mumbled, *"Je ne comprend pas,"* and left them. The next day he told the priest to ask London to brief more thoroughly the impetuous Americans who wanted to do it all alone.

CHAPTER VIII

Torigni and the surrounding area swarmed with Gestapo men who had been ordered to discover the identity of those who had been so successfully sabotaging railroad transport, and George passed the word to the priest to cease all activities except rescue work. The inactivity was too much for young Armand Owens to bear. The fourteen-year-old lad had been endowed with intelligence, a healthy body and a burning love for his country; nature had given him every gift except the all-important virtue of patience. Late one night he went off on his own. It had been weeks now since they had raided the ammunition dump; he felt it was time to gather some grenades. It was easy for him to slip through the hedge, to gather four grenades and to hide under the hedge until the sentry would pass. But this time the sentry did not pass. The dawn arrived early and sometimes suddenly in the Spring. The sun came up, peered over the horizon to thin the shadows of night, and the sentry saw the huddled form of the boy under the hedge. He grabbed him and three hours later word came to the priest of his capture. George walked into the church as usual a little before seven to be met by the saddened face of the priest.

"The boy said nothing," the priest told George. "He insisted that he had stolen the grenades as a prank. And he confessed to putting the cordite in the soup. He made them believe this, but they are to shoot him in the field behind the military post down the road. I am going . . ."

"No," George said sharply. "You cannot go there. They'll want to know how you found out the hour of the execution. They'll connect you with the boy. They might even make him talk by torturing you. You cannot go. Remain here, Père Gauraud, and pray for him," he said gently.

George hurried to the garage to pick up a tire he had repaired the day before. He rolled the tire down the road toward the military check point. A few men in uniform were standing outside the low barracks which housed the military headquarters for this small area. They looked at Pierre Touchette with disinterest. The garage helper returning a re-

paired tire was part of the normal village life. Pierre
had trouble rolling the tire. It fell several times
and he grinned foolishly. The soldiers chuckled
at the unco-ordinated muscular efforts of the half-
wit. *"Ein verrücktes Kind—nicht wahr? . . ."* one
of the men laughed. Yes, a real idiot, but quite
harmless. Someone inside barked an order and the
lounging Germans straightened up and entered the
building. George rolled his tire past the small
headquarters and then rolled it into the field adjacent to the building. This had been used for executions before. A sentry looked at him sharply and
then, when George muttered, *"C'est pour l'officier
—ce pneu là,"* the sentry shrugged his shoulders.
"Er ist beschäftigt," he said. *"Komm' später
wieder."* Yes, he was busy now, George knew, busy
shouting questions at the fourteen-year-old boy;
busy picking a firing squad to kill this boy. Never
had George hated war so much as at that moment.
His whole nature rebelled at what he would have
to watch in a moment. He could have saved this
boy by forbidding him to work with the Resistance
movement. He was too good, too fine and honest,
to die at fourteen. And he wasn't ready to die,
George felt. He wouldn't be ready until he was
able to accept the eternal truths. He was moving
toward understanding and faith, but he hadn't
quite reached them as yet. Six men marched stiffly
out of the barracks. Armand Owens, looking in-

credibly small and boyish and a little afraid, was led out between two enormous German soldiers. Perhaps they just looked enormous beside the boy. A young officer who led the execution squad glanced at Pierre, saw the foolish grin, saw him holding a heavy tire and turned away. They only walked twenty paces and then halted. Six men took their places, leaving the boy standing alone. Armand raised his eyes and saw George. His whole face changed. The fear left his eyes and he actually smiled. He turned his head away from George— even in this tragic hour he remembered not to identify himself with the garage helper—and then Armand Owens cried out in a loud steady voice, "Don't worry, God is with me." The short sentence was punctuated by the roar of six rifles, and the boy's body went spinning backwards to fall on the careless golden earth of this Normandy field.

Pierre walked to the front of the barracks. An officer, looking a little white, hurried out and jumped into a car which sped away. "The tire was for him," Pierre mumbled to the sentry.

"Get out," the German shouted angrily. Pierre trudged back to the village. He stopped at the church to find Père Gauraud on his knees. He put his arm around the little priest. "Your prayers were answered," he whispered. "The boy died with God's name on his lips."

CHAPTER IX

Two weeks later the Gestapo decided to teach the village of Torigni a lesson. There had been too much wrecking of trains and destruction of bridges, switches and viaducts; there was good reason to believe that little Torigni was helping Allied flyers along the road to safety; there had been too many incidents which showed that even the children were not showing the proper respect for the occupying forces. One morning two trucks filled with Gestapo men stormed into the village. They stopped in front of the garage and two Germans grabbed George and shoved him into one of the trucks. Within fifteen minutes they had herded together sixteen men and women; they had picked the first sixteen they had encountered on the street. George, at first convinced that someone had talked, now realized that he hadn't been singled out; the Germans had merely thrown out a net and he had been one of the unlucky fish to be caught. Only one of the troop besides George had been taken—the blacksmith Albert Baudouin. As he was shoved into the truck, protesting that he had work at his shop that had to be done for the military, he caught George's eye and winked. George knew that he wouldn't have to worry about the blacksmith talking. George was always apprehensive about men like Farmer Thibaut, who were sustained by sheer hatred for the Germans. He had little faith in hatred as a force that would endure under pressure. There came a time when you ran out of hatred. A youngster like Armand never ran out of love; an adventuresome man like the blacksmith would endure questioning and perhaps torture with the same spirit he had displayed in his sabotage work. Even the confinement and questioning would be part of the wonderful adventure the war had given him a chance to enjoy. George wondered as the trucks roared on toward Saint-Lô how he himself would react under Gestapo pressure. Ah, well, he was a professional, he assured himself; professionals took it as long as they had to take it; professionals had no right to break down. As to the others, George wasn't worried. The farmers and shopkeepers who had been caught in the net knew nothing.

As for himself, as long as he was Pierre Touchette he would be safe. If he ever relaxed, ever permitted a flash of George DuPre to show through the fumbling, unco-ordinated personality which was Pierre Touchette, he would be lost. It was a long time since he had allowed himself the luxury of any emotion. He was nothing but a mental machine, and he had no doubts at all that he could keep on thinking clearly without surrendering to any emotion—even pain. He felt no conceit over this. It was merely a tribute to those nine months of intensive training he had undergone. He felt now that the mental state induced by his instructors was about to pay off. An agent, in discussing the effect of torture, had said, "You could even get used to hanging--if you could hang long enough." Well, he told himself grimly, he soon might find out about that.

The trucks drew up in front of Gestapo headquarters in Saint-Lô. It was a large building which had once been a veterinary hospital. In back of it there was a high-walled courtyard, and it was here that the Gestapo carried out executions. The sixteen men and women of Torigni were shoved into the building, led below into what had been the basement stables, and put into individual cells. George knew the geography of the building well. Two months before a British pilot had been caught and held in the Gestapo headquarters for questioning. George and the troop had discussed plans for rescuing him, and Saint-Lô Resistance men had furnished them with the complete plans of the building. The basement originally contained four large stalls for sick horses. Each stall had been partitioned off into four cubicles which now served as cells. There were sixteen in all; just enough to accommodate the sixteen prisoners. George found that he couldn't stretch out in his cell. He could lie down only when he drew his knees up to his chest. The cell measured four and a half feet by three feet. He had been huddling there only half an hour when the air became intolerably warm. He knew then that the Gestapo was beginning the softening-up process. The Saint-Lô Resistance men had told them of this. There was a huge furnace in the cellar below the basement, originally intended to keep sick horses warm. Vents had been built into the stalls to bring the hot air from furnace to horse. The Gestapo now utilized it to bring hot air from furnace to prisoners. Soon George was sweating profusely. Two hours of this and the air cooled. Now George knew that below in the cellar the furnace vents had been closed and vents leading to an air conditioner opened. The Gestapo had developed this alternate hot-and-cold treatment as a quick method of reducing the physical and mental resistance of prisoners.

It helped to know what was coming, George felt. It was the unknown which was the most frightening. He began to feel the air chill. It had been somewhere in the neighborhood of 120 degrees; now it dropped to 30 degrees. This alternate frying and freezing kept up for twenty-four hours, during which only a slice of bread and a pan of water were shoved into George's cell. The treatment did dehydrate you; it did weaken you, and if you had a tendency to pneumonia it would kill you. But George was in good health; the hot-and-cold air treatment annoyed him and made him uncomfortable, but beyond that did no harm. Four days passed. Twice a day bread and water was served— nothing else. George knew that he was weaker than when he had been picked up, but his mental faculties hadn't been blunted. Occasionally he heard men being led from their cells; now and then a shrill scream of pain penetrated his cubicle, but beyond that—silence. On the fourth day the door of his cell opened and he was commanded to follow the guard. He was led upstairs to an interrogation room.

There was a desk in the room, two chairs and a table to which was attached an ordinary carpenter's vise. A major sat behind the desk. Two assistants—a sergeant and a corporal—took hold of George. The major, a thin nervous man of about fifty, looked with disgust at the filthy caricature of a man who stood before him drooling and whimpering.

"This is Pierre Touchette, the garage helper," the sergeant said.

"The man is an idiot," the major barked angrily. "Why waste my time with this fool?"

"Even an idiot may know the names of the Resistance men," the sergeant said. "They say he has the mind of an eight-year-old boy. I think we can make any eight-year-old boy tell what he knows."

"All right," the major nodded. "Have you ever seen any English flyers near your village?"

Pierre shrugged his shoulders in feigned hopeless bewilderment and shook his head. The corporal had moved away from him. The sergeant was holding his right arm. Then the sergeant's own right arm swung. The blow landed on the bridge of George's nose; there was a blinding stab of pain and he felt the sickening crunching of the smashed cartilage. He swayed, moaning and whimpering as Pierre Touchette would moan and whimper, and then the sharp pain receded. "Tell us the truth, you pig," the sergeant roared.

"*Je ne sais pas,*" he mumbled.

Who heads the Resistance in Torigni? Who blew up the bridges? Who steals dynamite from the ammunition dump? Who rescues English flyers? The questions followed each other rapidly. The thin major was getting impatient at Pierre's mumbled answers that he knew nothing.

"With the major's permission may I question the

115

prisoner?" the sergeant asked. The major nodded. The sergeant shoved Pierre close to the table on which the vise was attached. He inserted the index finger of George's right hand into the clamp of the vise and then slowly closed the vise on the finger.

"Who in your village is in the Resistance?" he barked.

Pierre shook his head and then the sergeant kicked his feet from under him; his body went sprawling to the floor but the finger remained in the vise. It snapped like a broken toothpick and the pain of it sent a searing hot needle into George's brain. He climbed slowly to his feet. The sergeant unclamped the vise to release the finger. The broken bone stuck through the flesh. Something one of the agents had said at the Oxford school flashed through George's mind. He had been tortured by the Gestapo and had been released. "The greater the pain," he had said, "the quicker nature acts with its own anaesthetic." It was true, George realized. His broken nose was merely a numbed portion of his face now. The quick agony of the snapped finger had receded in the matter of a minute, and now the whole hand was becoming numb. He looked down at the bloody finger almost dispassionately, objectively, as though he were looking at something not part of him at all.

"You have more fingers," the sergeant said coldly. "We have more questions."

"I know nothing," Pierre mumbled.

"Take him away," the major said in disgust. "I don't think he does know anything."

The sergeant's face fell. "If you'd give me another half hour, Major."

"Later," the major showed irritation. "We have others to question."

The sergeant grabbed Pierre by the hair. He looked into his eyes. "Think it over, idiot," he snarled. "We will let you go now, but you will be back soon."

He pushed Pierre toward the door. The guard outside looked at his blood-covered face without interest and shoved him toward the iron steps that led to the basement. Back in his cell George took stock. There was nothing he could do about his nose, but he could perhaps help the finger. He ripped a piece of cloth from his shirt tail, shoved the protruding bone back into its sheath of skin, tried to put the two broken ends together and then bound the finger tightly with the cloth. He felt uncomfortable, but the pain was not unbearable. There was one bright spot in what was otherwise a hopeless predicament. They didn't suspect him of being anything but a half-witted garage helper. It was sheer misfortune that he had been one of the sixteen caught in the net. As long as he could maintain his role he and his secrets were safe.

They fed him some bread and horse meat that

night. Two days later he was again led upstairs. This room had only one chair, but no desk. The chair had arms, and leather straps were attached to the arms and to the legs. His first thought was that this was an electric chair. The major was not present this time. The sergeant was in command of this operation and from the expression on his face George felt that he was enjoying every minute of it. He was a short, stocky man with dark-brown eyes and heavy eyebrows. His nose was almost flat and his mouth merely a tight line in an impassive face. The face looked as though it had never smiled.

The corporal shoved him into the chair. He strapped his legs and then strapped his left wrist to the arm of the chair. On the right arm of the chair there was a pad of white paper. The corporal placed a pencil in George's right hand and then lifted his arm to rest it on the pad. Then he pushed George's head back. "Open your mouth," he barked. When George obeyed, the corporal shoved a clamp between his teeth. It forced the mouth wide open. The sergeant went to a corner of the room and wheeled a table close to the chair. George looked at it and saw that it wasn't actually a table; it was a portable three-burner electric stove. On each burner there stood a kettle. The sergeant inserted a plug into a wall socket. He said nothing at all, and George looked at him in some wonder. This man was obviously a sadist who received the same stimulation watching others suffer as normal men did making love or drinking or listening to great music. He had heard of such men, but had never met one before.

A completely extraneous thought gripped his mind as he watched the three burners take on a dull red glow. He had once been angered by a book which had portrayed the Eskimos as cruel, heartless people. The book had dwelt almost gloatingly on the Eskimo habit of taking the very old or hopelessly crippled out of the igloo and allowing them to die in the numbing cold of the Arctic. The book had not explained the reason for the custom. Eskimos had to follow the food supply. They might spend three months fishing and hunting in an area and then the fish would disappear and the caribou and polar bear would be frightened off. In desperation, they would eat their dogs, and now they had their choice of starving or moving to a new territory. The trip to a new hunting and fishing area would be tortuous. Only the strongest could stand such a journey. The old and infirm would suffer horribly, and because they would have to be lashed to sleds which would be hand drawn by the strong, the trip would take a long time. The old would most certainly be dead by the time the new area was reached, and the added exertion of pulling the sled would take its toll of the others. And so they would move the aged and infirm out of the igloos and leave them alone in the snow to die. Freezing to death was almost painless; it was like dropping into a deep sleep. The bitter cold acted as an anaesthetic. The custom was not born of cruelty but of compassion, and George had always disliked the man who had so maligned the Eskimos. They were realists, but were never cruel merely for the sake of satisfying some unnatural emotion. But this sergeant seemed to enjoy inflicting suffering.

The kettles were singing now. Home in Winnipeg he'd always liked that sound. He'd walk into his home out of the thirty-below weather of January, hurry to the kitchen and Muriel would be sitting there spreading jam on a piece of bread for him, and then he'd hear the singing of the kettle. He'd lost his English accent, but had never lost his desire for tea in the late afternoon.

"You will answer my questions," the sergeant said in oddly sounding guttural French. "You cannot talk so you will write the answers on this pad. Now give me the names of those in the Resistance in Torigni."

George shook his head, rolling his eyes in feigned desperation. The sergeant grabbed the first kettle, lifted it and poured the hot water into George's open mouth. He choked on the water, but it wasn't too hot as yet. For two minutes the sergeant snapped questions at George, and when George continued to shake his head he actually noticed an expression of satisfaction flash into the dark-brown eyes of the sergeant. He took the second kettle and poured about a cup of water into George's mouth. It was hot, but still not boiling. It stung the roof of his mouth. He tried hard not to swallow all of it. If he could retain some of it in his mouth it would dilute the boiling water which was coming next. He leaned his head back to keep the water in his mouth from trickling down his chin.

"Your last chance," the sergeant said coldly. "Write down the names of those who blew up the bridge. Write just one name and we will release you. Your hand does not write. You refuse? Very well."

He reached for the third kettle. He lifted it above George's head, aimed for the mouth and poured. George braced himself mentally, but there was no way to ease the horrible pain of boiling water meeting the soft tissues of the palate and gums. He had retained some of the water from the second kettle; it did dilute the boiling water slightly, but the agony was intense. The sergeant put the kettle back on the burner and George allowed his head to fall forward on his chest.

"The fool has fainted," the sergeant said in disgust.

"It could be that the half-wit can't write," the corporal shrugged his shoulders.

"I never thought of that," the sergeant muttered. "If he knows anything he'll talk now."

They unloosened the straps and pulled George to his feet. Burnt flesh apparently was not allowed nature's quick anaesthetic, George decided. The pain in his mouth seemed to increase. It traveled as though by osmosis down into his larynx and to his lower throat. It was the kind of pain that made you writhe; not the quick stab of pain that is soon over, but a slow agony that seems to be mounting in a very crescendo of pain.

They pushed him from the room and he was led back to his cell. He huddled miserably on the cement floor, hoping, trying desperately to find oblivion from the pain in sleep. But he couldn't sleep. The pain stayed with him.

They left him alone for two days and then he was brought again to the interrogation room in which he had first been questioned. They left him alone for a few minutes. A window looked out on the courtyard. He heard some commands and then six men walked by the window. Behind them was a man dressed in the uniform of an RAF pilot. They disappeared, and then he heard the command to halt. There was silence for a few moments and then a volley of fire. The six Germans marched past the window again without the man in the RAF uniform. Had he in fact been an RAF pilot? George doubted it very much. The major and his two assistants entered the room.

"You are hiding valuable information," the major said sharply. "This is your last chance to talk. Give us the names of the Resistance members in Torigni."

"*Je ne sais rien,*" George mumbled. "*Pourquoi me frappez-vous?*"

"Why do we beat you?" the major repeated his question. "Because you are a traitor who has worked against us. I am sick and tired of you." He turned to the sergeant. "Take him out and shoot him."

The sergeant pushed him from the room. The same firing squad he had seen pass outside the window was waiting. It's just a cheap trick, George told himself. His nine months of training had convinced him that this was a typical Gestapo maneuver; they had told him to expect it. And when they ordered him into the courtyard he marched with confident steps. The sergeant directed him to stand against the wall. The wall was pockmarked with bullet holes, and there was a dark pool of what looked like dried blood below it. "Probably cattle blood," George said to himself. The six men carrying guns lined up twenty paces away. The sergeant shouted a command and the men raised their rifles. "They're bluffing," George told himself with desperate insistence. They hadn't even blindfolded him. Another command and he heard the click as trigger guards were released. Perhaps they weren't bluffing after all. If he were to die now, it would be as the whimpering Pierre Touchette; he couldn't even straighten up and die decently, as young Armand had died with the name of his Creator on his lips. He looked into the barrels of six guns and then waited for the command to fire. It never came. Instead there was a shout from the doorway out of which they had emerged a few moments before. It was the major who had called, "Stop. Take him back to his cell."

The sergeant spun him around and headed him toward the door. He followed him down the steps to the basement. A guard opened the cell door and the sergeant, beside himself with rage, shrieked, "You'll talk tomorrow," and then he swung his right hand. It landed on the smashed nose and again George heard the cartilage give way. He didn't fall, but stood there swaying, and the sergeant threw a tremendous punch that hit George on the point of the jaw. The sergeant was wearing a heavy ring. It opened the skin as neatly as though it had been a scalpel, and George collapsed to the floor. The sergeant pushed him into the cell and slammed the door.

He had three days of respite. He couldn't eat either the bread or the scraps of half-cooked horse meat they threw him. It was sheer agony to swallow. It even hurt to drink the tepid water they brought him. He dozed off occasionally, but it was the collapse of exhaustion rather than the soothing sleep that renews energy. When he awoke he found that his chin had stopped bleeding. They must let him go now, he felt. They thought of him as a half-wit; had he been a half-wit and had he known anything, he would most certainly have talked by now.

He was rather surprised that he felt no fear. He had never thought of himself as a brave man, but now he felt no fear at all. It puzzled him. George DuPre was a man without conceit; he thought of himself as the average man with only the average talents, the average skills, the average man's breaking point. "You can't have guts without God." Where had he heard that? The phrase kept ringing in his ears, and then he remembered the Commando instructor who had said it to him. He had faith all right; perhaps that's why he wasn't really afraid at this moment. What was fear anyhow? he asked himself. He answered his own question. Fear was a lack of trust in God. Christ showed no fear when they nailed him to the Cross. His faith in His Father was so great that there was no room for fear in his heart. George lay on the cement floor, smelling the sour odor of his own sweat and his own filth, his face and mouth and throat one whole mass of pain, and yet for the moment he felt almost lifted above his pain. He'd discovered a weapon with which he could fight these men—the weapon of faith. The whole purpose of their torture was to instill such a degree of fear that the will power would be destroyed and their victim would blurt out everything he knew. He knew now that he would never talk— fear could never stand up against faith.

He considered almost with detachment the fact that not even under the gravest stress had he ever cried out in English. The odd thing about it was that he did not have to control any urge to use English. He had taken his beating as a half-wit would have taken it; even when his mind had been distorted by pain he had only used the badly accented French of Pierre Touchette. George DuPre lay deep in the realm of his subconscious, to be summoned occasionally when he was completely alone, but George DuPre never appeared when to do so would be to invite disaster. Even now, he told himself, he was not thinking as George DuPre; he was thinking as an anonymous British agent who merely had a number and who had been well trained for the ordeal he had just undergone and would continue to undergo.

The experts back at the school had been absolutely right about the intelligence of the Gestapo. They lived by force. It was the only weapon they knew how to use. Their clumsy attempts to use the psychological approach were too obvious to be successful. "Tell us the truth and we will let you go," was the constant refrain from major and sergeant. He knew this for a lie. He knew that once they had wrung the truth from a man they immediately shot him. Your only chance for survival was to maintain an appearance of ignorance. George breathed a prayer of thanks that Armand Owens had been caught not by the Gestapo but by the regular army men. Their questioning was always persistent and usually skillful, but if a prisoner refused to talk they admitted defeat. If the prisoner was guilty, as Armand had been guilty, they shot him immediately, but in this area at least the army had never resorted to torture. There was a rigid army tradition comparable to the traditions of the British army, and for the most part German military authorities abided by it. A pilot who had been captured and had subsequently escaped had told the little priest in George's presence how they operated. They would take the pilot's name and serial number, and if he refused to give further information they accepted the situation with apparent good grace. They would recall him a day or two later.

"Your name is Smith and your serial number is 156,890, you say," an interrogating officer would go on amiably. "Sit down, have a cigarette—you'll find Players there in the box. Now let me tell you some more about yourself. You were born in Tunbridge Wells in Kent and you attended Westminster School. You trained at Yorkshire in the north and then became part of Squadron 702 stationed at Biggin Hill. Your C.O. was the late Wing Commander Douglas Bevan. During the Battle of Britain you won the D.S.O. Casualties were high. Five of your original squadron were killed. You shot down eight of our planes and you were promoted to Squadron Leader. During the past six months you have been stationed at Northolt; nice place, only a stone's throw from London. You lads usually frequented the Boar's Head pub, however, on the Great North Road. Two months ago Reggie Ashford and James Barlow of your squadron were posted as missing. You might be glad to know that they are quite safe, and they're smart enough to know that the war is about over. You British have resisted magnificently, but Churchill is the only one who thinks that Britain still has a chance, and the admirable Churchill is first of all a politician who has to hold such views. Now both Ashford and Barlow are realists. They have told us all this and a good deal more, too. Frankly, we have no desire to treat you as anything but an officer and a gentleman. Why not accept the inevitable, answer a few questions and we'll send you to join Ashford and Barlow in a very pleasant rest camp outside Munich. . . ."

"If you aren't careful," the pilot had told Père Gauraud, "you find yourself hypnotized by these interrogators. They seem to know everything;

they're masters of psychology. They treat you damn well, feed you and give you an occasional bottle of beer. It's hard to resist them. I'm afraid some of the boys might have spilled everything they know. These chaps keep their promises, too. If you open up and talk, they have nothing but contempt for you, but they do treat you well. If you keep your mouth shut, they respect you and treat you as a fellow officer. They say the Gestapo works quite differently."

Two days later they called for George again. This time he was brought to a different room. The walls were of white tile. The sergeant and the corporal were alone in the room. George reasoned that this must have been the operating room when the building had been a veterinary hospital. He was told to stand against the wall, facing it. They pointed where they wanted him, and then he saw that there were straps hanging from the wall. They joined the straps in back of him and pulled them tight. Now for some strange reason he was strapped to the wall. But it wasn't a wall. It was actually the top of a large operating table used for horses. He felt his feet rising as the bottom of the table was lifted. Finally it flattened out. They pulled his legs apart. Now he lay face down, spread-eagled on the enormous operating table.

The sergeant called out loudly, and a door to the right opened. Although his body was strapped to

the table, George could move his head. He turned
his eyes. A pleasant-looking girl with a friendly
smile on her face walked through the door. In one
hand she carried a pair of shears; the other held a
heavy syringe filled with a colorless liquid. George
recognized it as the type of syringe used to give
horses enemas; the needle was blunted. The girl
approached the table and without a word cut
through the back of his trousers with her shears.
He felt hopelessly naked and exposed. Then the
sergeant said, "Give him a dose of it." He felt a hot
stream being directed at his lower limbs. It stung
badly, but the pain wasn't sharp enough to make
him cry out. The odor was familiar. It was a long
time since he'd studied chemistry at Cambridge,
but he recognized the smell of sulphuric acid.

"That is just a sample," the sergeant yelled at
him, "to show you we mean business. Tell us who
blew up the bridges."

"*Je ne sais pas*," he muttered. "*Pourquoi me
tourmentez-vous?*"

"Why do we torture you?" the sergeant
screamed. "Because you won't tell us what you
know. Give him a real dose this time."

He reached down and stretched George's legs
far apart. George felt the nozzle of the syringe part-
ing his buttocks, and then the fiery liquid touched
the most tender part of his flesh. He screamed with
agony as the strong stream from the syringe pene-

trated into his rectum. The agony spread through his intestines and bowels; it seemed to fill his whole abdominal cavity. His senses began to reel, but he tried desperately to hang on to consciousness. He knew if he fainted he might cry out in his delirium. He banged his head on the table trying to shock himself into mental clarity. The girl had stopped now. He turned his head and saw her leave, a faint smile of satisfaction on her face. The sergeant bellowed the familiar questions again, but George only moaned, *"Je ne sais pas . . . je ne sais pas . . ."*

The straps were unfastened and they pulled him to his feet. He tried to stand up, but the agony doubled him over. "Stand up," the sergeant yelled, and he tried to straighten George up with a right-hand punch. It landed on the battered nose, but George hardly felt the lesser pain in the consuming agony of the fire that was searing his body. He stumbled down the stairs and fell into his cell. He lay on the cement with his knees doubled up to ease the pain. But he had a strange feeling of triumph in addition to the pain. What else could they do? They had subjected his body to every kind of indignity and yet they hadn't been able to break him. They had failed. He breathed a prayer of thanks to the One who had made his faith strong enough to withstand the torture. He'd never thought of himself as a religious man back in Canada. He felt rather vaguely that he was a practical Christian; he embraced no inflexible dogmas. But now he found that he was clinging to his faith and wrapping it around himself as a protective garment.

Even at that moment, lying on the rough cement of the cell, he couldn't find it in his heart to hate the sergeant or the pleasant-faced girl. An instructor at the school, in discussing the bestiality of the Gestapo, had said, "Hitler, in an early speech, said, 'Give me the children and I will rule the world.' They gave him their children and he put them into his Hitler Jugend and made them after his image. He taught them to hate; he managed to stamp out their innate feelings of decency. They grew up in his philosophy and were never taught any other. Charity, kindness, love of mankind—they were taught that these were decadent emotions unworthy of a soldier of the Third Reich."

The words of the instructor came back to him now. No, you couldn't blame the sadistic sergeant or the girl; they had been trained for this since childhood. The girl didn't look more than twenty-two or twenty-three. Once these two had been normal six- or seven-pound babies; once they had nursed at a mother's breast, played and cried as all babies play and cry. And then the system began to mold them. They had never been given the chance to live normal lives; they had learned that cruelty to enemies of their state was the highest form of loyalty to the state.

George thought of his early days as a Boy Scout, and he felt that the lessons he'd learned then were helping him now. He remembered the childish pledges the Scouts made, and now they didn't seem childish at all. It was then that he resolved that if he survived, he would dedicate his life to helping organizations like the Scouts. This was his last thought before he fell into a half sleep, half stupor. When he awoke it was to see the face of a guard bending over him. "Get out," the guard said. George blinked in bewilderment. "Get out," the guard shouted. "You can go. You are free."

CHAPTER X

He climbed shakily to his feet. He couldn't straighten up. He took a few hesitant steps. The guard pushed him on his way. It was agony to climb the stairs. He could feel warm blood running down the backs of his thighs. He reached the door and the guard shoved him out. It was dark. He walked away from the building where horses had once been treated. Every step was torture, but he kept walking. The streets were deserted; it was obviously close to curfew. A man in the dress of a factory worker brushed against him and whispered, "Follow me." He followed the man nearly a mile, and then his unknown guide turned into an apartment house. George followed him up one flight of stairs, and then a door opened and he stumbled into a lighted room.

134

others. His shack had been cleaned in his absence. There were actually sheets on his cot. Georges Lavelle helped him inside and his anxious face reflected the affection he felt for his helper. They all knew what he had gone through; they all knew that he hadn't betrayed them when betrayal could have been excused. They looked at him with considerable awe; none of them felt that he had the courage to stand against the kind of torture he had been made to endure.

Doctor Rennet was ready with vegetable oils and with soothing boric-acid enemas and with salt-water rinses for the bleeding tissues of his mouth. He made George spend two weeks in bed. For a week he could swallow nothing but soup, and then the doctor coaxed him with soft-boiled eggs. Every night Gerard Benois would drop by with a bottle of cider; he knew this to be the only drink George liked. The cool locally made cider soothed his throat. Gradually some of the pain left him, or perhaps he had become so accustomed to it that he had come to accept it as normal. He asked the doctor about that.

"It could be," he nodded thoughtfully. "If I had you in a hospital I would be keeping you under morphine or some such drug. But I have had no drugs of that nature for a long time. Yet you have survived. The truth is that man is the most adaptable animal in the world. He can endure pain that no animal can endure. If a bull, for instance, is in pain he will go berserk and perhaps dash his skull into the nearest stone. But somehow man manages to conquer his pain."

It was two weeks before George returned to activity. Now again each morning he went to mass to listen to the little priest deliver messages from London. More British and American pilots came to Farmer Thibaut's home to be interrogated by Père Gauraud. Once more Pierre Touchette, the half-wit, would listen to them and when satisfied that they were what they appeared to be, would nod, and they would be passed on to the next step in the Rat Run. It was late 1943 now, and the little priest who kept records of the escapees who had been aided told George that 152 British and American airmen had been passed on to safety since he had arrived in 1940.

The priest filled George in on the news. Sabotage had been stepped up considerably. In addition to dynamite and grenades, small Sten guns had been dropped and they had been buried to await the day they would be needed. The German submarine warfare had been very successful, and London was very concerned, Père Gauraud said. Then one night the priest came to him with a message from London. George was to proceed immediately to the village of Bernay, some forty miles north. There he should contact the head of the local Resistance

troop. That was all. Neither he nor the priest had
any idea what London had in mind, but by now
George obeyed blindly with complete confidence
that every order was part of a larger plan that
would gradually emerge.

"We will miss you, Pierre." The little priest
pressed his arm. "You are not of my faith, but
you are a good man and you will know that
wherever you are I will be remembering you in
my prayers each morning."

"Thank you, Père Gauraud." George was touched by the warm affection the little priest felt for
him.

"London must realize that you have done your
job here well. Our escape route is functioning
beautifully. That is why you are no longer needed
here, I suppose. When you reach Bernay get in
touch with Rene Godbout, a farmer who lives just
outside the village."

CHAPTER XI

George left Torigni at dawn. He carried only his identification papers, some bread and cheese, and a few hundred francs. He still wore the same oil-soaked clothes in which he had landed three years before. Twice since then new shoes had been issued to him, but nothing else. He shambled out of the village before it was awake and headed for Bernay. Bernay was merely a larger edition of Torigni. George went from shop to shop asking if anyone needed a porter. He wanted no money, he said. He would work for his food and lodging. He was a good worker, he insisted eagerly; he could sweep and clean and he was strong, too, he said. Most of the shopkeepers looked either contemptuously or pityingly at the drooling half-wit who talked such execrable French with such a strong

Normandy accent. No one could ever mistake a man from Normandy. Generations ago the Swedes had emigrated to Normandy and they had given the Normans the heritage of their tall strong bodies and they had touched the speech of Normans with a Swedish accent that had survived to this day. Even this poor, dim-witted fool spoke French with a Swedish accent. Finally a baker told him he could sweep out his shop twice a day in return for bread and cheese. He could sleep in the kitchen close to the warm ovens.

Two days later Pierre Touchette walked out beyond the village to find the farmer Godbout. He disliked having to ask the whereabouts of the Resistance man; instead, he stopped at each farm asking if an extra hand was needed. One sympathetic woman looked at him not with contempt but with pity, and when she gave him a glass of cider he told her he had heard that a farmer named Godbout was looking for help to harvest his crop. Did he live in this neighborhood?

"Yes, the poor man lives just down the road," she said rather sadly. "Rene Godbout was once our village banker, as his father had been before him. But the Boches took over his bank and he went to this small farm he owned. Now he is a farmer, which is harder work than being a banker."

Pierre Touchette mumbled an agreement, finished his cider and went on to the farm owned by

Rene Godbout. The farmer was in the field wielding a scythe. He listened with indifference to Pierre's request for work.

"Where do you come from?" he asked casually.

"From Torigni," George said. "There was no more work there. I came here hoping to find work."

"What is the name of the priest in Torigni?" the farmer asked, never stopping his scythe.

"Père Gauraud of St. Peter's. He told me to look for you."

The farmer dropped his scythe. "Sit down." He wiped the perspiration from his face. "I have been expecting you."

"Can you tell me what my orders are?" George asked.

The farmer nodded. "We have contacts with the Gestapo in this district. We heard the other day that they are desperately short of forced labor in Germany. A recent bombing killed half of the workers in the great submarine plant at Hamburg. The Gestapo has been ordered to round up several hundred men to be sent there. They have decided to find them here and in a few villages nearby. I informed London of this. We have orders to see that some of our men are to be included. Some may be sent to Hamburg. It is important that we get some of our men there."

"And then . . ."

The farmer shrugged his shoulders. "Somehow

London will get word to you. Headquarters has sent one general order. 'It is necessary to sink the U-boats before they get wet.' "

George smiled at that. It was so typical of the terse orders he had been receiving for three years now. He walked to the farmer's kitchen with him and accepted some bread and cheese. The farmer talked bitterly of the Germans and of what they had done to him. He talked of the prosperous little bank which had been in his family for three generations. It was all gone now, he said. Once again George was struck by the strange brand of patriotism displayed by men like Godbout. Godbout hated the Germans because they had ruined him financially, because they had taken from him what he considered to be his birthright—the village bank. He never mentioned France. His life was bounded by the outer limits of the town of Bernay. This town was his France, and his hatred was a personal one. He hated the Germans as he would have hated thieves who had broken into his bank and stolen from it. It was this hatred—and no love for his country—which sustained him. George hoped that his hatred lasted.

"Stay outside the bakery as much as possible," Godbout warned. "When they come they will first grab those on the street."

George returned to Bernay. He arose early each morning, grabbed a broom and swept the pavement outside the bakery. No sidewalk in the history of the town had ever been so thoroughly swept and scrubbed. The baker would laugh at his earnest helper and tell him that the inside of the shop needed occasional attention too. George would nod amiably, mutter an incomprehensible agreement and hurriedly clean the kitchens and the floor of the bakery. Then he would return to the pavement to sweep away vigorously. Nothing happened for two weeks, though George did notice that a great many men seemed to be idling in front of the café and post office. Sometimes they would laugh good-naturedly at the industrious half-wit who couldn't get the street in front of the baker's shop clean enough. Some, George noticed, didn't laugh. Two or three seemed to look with approval at him. He had no way of knowing whether these were Resistance men or whether any of them knew that he was one of them. When they tried to draw him into conversation he'd mutter, "*J'ai du travail à faire*," and turn away. He had received no orders to contact anyone other than farmer Godbout, and he would keep it that way. He remembered wryly something his father had said to a young subaltern twenty years before. "The way to become successful in the Royal Artillery is to keep your mouth shut and never volunteer." That seemed to be a good rule in Intelligence work, too, George felt. For three years he had obeyed every order blindly

and he had survived and had never been suspected.
He would continue to have faith in his London
superiors and perhaps he could continue to survive, and do a useful job of work.

One morning while George was pushing the inevitable broom, trucks roared into Bernay. George
straightened up and for once tried to look a little
unlike Pierre Touchette. They might not accept a
half-wit even for forced labor. But these Gestapo
men who swarmed out of the trucks so eagerly
were not interested in quality but in quantity.
They had been ordered to pick up sixty men.
George was one of the first to be hurled into a
truck. Some of the men who had been idling in
front of the café put up a half-hearted fight, but
they were quickly subdued and ordered into the
open trucks. George caught the eye of one of them;
he was grinning with satisfaction. Within twenty
minutes the Gestapo had its quota. Some of the
older men they had caught were crying piteously,
pleading to be released. Women came running to
reach up for husbands or sons, but the guards
brushed them away. These women knew that forced
laborers seldom returned. They were as expendable
as bullets to the Germans. If they could get a few
months' work out of a man before he collapsed,
they were satisfied. Some women screamed impre-
cations at the Germans, others fainted, and then the
trucks pulled away to leave a village out of which

the heart had been torn. The trucks sped through the quiet countryside and farmers bending over their crops straightened up to watch their neighbors being sent to slavery. They probably thanked God that they were farmers; farmers were needed in occupied France. The trucks turned off the road, bumped across a field and stopped at a railway siding. A train was waiting. Other trucks had already discharged the human crops which had been harvested at other villages in the area. George and the men of Bernay were told to get into the train. Within fifteen minutes the locomotive drew the train away.

"They generally use cattle cars. We are lucky," one of the men cried out gaily. George looked at him closely. It was the man who had grinned so with contentment when he had been caught. He was obviously a Resistance man—too obvious, George felt. He should have played the role of a bitter, reluctant, enraged citizen. But perhaps he, like the blacksmith Baudouin, was a man who loved adventure for its own sake and was savoring this experience and couldn't help but show his enjoyment. The day coaches were comfortable enough. The train crawled slowly north. Late that afternoon the men were served black bread and sausage—German army rations.

"They make this stuff out of sawdust," one of the men growled.

146

"Better than horse meat," another said.

For the most part the men were silent. Some, torn from families, were deep in despair. Others seemed dazed by the quick turn of events that had torn them from their normal lives and precipitated them into what seemed a hideous nightmare. Some appeared to accept their fate stoically.

The train traveled all night, always going north. The second day passed slowly. The weather had turned cold and the cars were unheated. Again they were fed bread, sausage and some cheese. Several of the men tried to engage George in conversation. He turned a blank, unheeding face toward them. *"Laissez moi tranquil,"* he'd mumble, and discouraged by his silence they gave up.

That night the Allied bombers came over. The blacked-out train stopped. George could hear the rhythmic beat of the four-engined planes perhaps twenty thousand feet above. He could hear the scream of the big bombs cutting through the air and then the blast of the explosion seemed to rock the train. The train itself was obviously not the target. The planes may have been after factories in the neighborhood; it may have been bridges they were after. But the bombs fell uncomfortably close, and George felt a great sense of relief when the accustomed silence returned to the night and the train began to move forward.

CHAPTER XII

The next morning the train stopped four miles outside of Hamburg. Once more British Intelligence had been right. It looked very much, George thought, as though he would soon be working in one of Germany's most important plants. The men (there were about 250 in all) were ordered off the train. They were herded into groups, and now a dozen officials began to walk around them, inspecting them, appraising them much as a farmer would appraise cattle he was considering purchasing. None of the officials gave George more than a cursory glance. From their conversation George realized that these men were factory supervisors. Each apparently had charge of a different department, and each was trying to pick out the healthiest workers available. The youngest and strongest men went quickly. Soon George was standing alone with three others. He had a moment of panic lest he be found unacceptable. He straightened up and for the moment allowed his face to assume a look of reasonable intelligence.

One of the supervisors muttered, "I need another porter. This fool should be able to keep the place clean."

He motioned George to join a group of about thirty others who would work in his particular department. Now they were all marched to the camp, a mile away, which would be their home as long as they could perform their duties. The camp was composed of dozens of low, squat buildings, each housing seventy men. When they were herded into the hut, a camp guard told them briefly their duties. They would work in the submarine plant which was just a mile away. They would march to the plant at five every morning. There was a stove at one end of the hut, and an individual army mess kit for each of the hut's inmates.

"Every morning at four A.M.," the guard barked, "food for the day will be delivered here. You will cook the food yourself. Appoint your own cooks. It is their responsibility to see to it that the food is evenly divided. Any man who complains that he is not getting enough to eat is a liar. If he isn't given enough, it is because the cooks you yourselves appoint have stolen the food."

The next day George and the other sixty-nine oc-
cupants of the hut were marched to the plant.
George had already noticed that at least thirty of
the men in his group had come from Bernay.
Among them was the big, smiling man who had
been so obviously happy to be among those picked
up. He marched next to George en route to the
plant that first morning. He told George that his
name was Felix Dumont.

"Rene Godbout is my good friend," he whispered
to George. "He told me to make contact with you."

"All right, all right," George said impatiently.
"But you talk too much."

Felix Dumont laughed. "There is little left for
us Frenchmen to do but talk," he said. "And who
can hear us? These Germans are such fools. They
picked sixty of us up in Bernay. They do not even
know that fifteen of us were there waiting to be
picked up. Yes," he chuckled, "they have done
something we could never do. We could never
smuggle fifteen Resistance men into this factory.
The stupid Gestapo have done what DeGaulle himself could not do. Thank God they do not leave jobs
like this to the German military. Tell me, Pierre
Touchette," he asked curiously, "just who are you?"

"I am a garage helper from Torigni," George
mumbled. "That is all."

Felix Dumont looked amused. "All right, all
right," he said soothingly. "I only know that Rene

Godbout told us that if we did manage to get into this factory we should report anything of interest to you."

"Godbout talks too much," George mumbled. "So do you. Don't talk at all. Just keep your ears open . . . I am Pierre Touchette," he drooled. "A garage helper. That is all you need to know."

Felix Dumont looked at him curiously, then lapsed into silence. Farmer Rene Godbout had undoubtedly meant well, but he had not learned the lesson of blind obedience so essential to the success of Intelligence operations. Godbout, George felt, had no idea who he really was. He just assumed because of messages from Torigni and from London that Pierre Touchette was a man of some importance in the Resistance movement. Perhaps he felt that the role of half-wit was an assumed role. But beyond that he knew nothing. George didn't want his well-meaning but too enthusiastic, new-found friend Dumont to know anything beyond that either.

The seventy men were passed through a heavily guarded gate and marched to a one-story building. The supervisor who had selected them the day before was there to receive them. This was a machine shop. The seventy forced laborers would for the most part be used to carry heavy raw materials into the spacious shed and then, when the skilled workers on the lathes and drill presses had turned out a finished product, they would carry these to another shed. The supervisor singled out George and four others and told them that they would be responsible for keeping the floors clean. George and the others soon settled into the routine of life as forced laborers.

The food dumped at the entrance to their shed each morning was nothing but horse meat and black bread. Two of the men who had been cooks were put in charge of the food. But they could do little to make the boiled horse meat palatable. They were not given any salt or seasoning of any kind. Once or twice a week they were given a few turnips and potatoes out of which they made a thin soup. After two weeks of this George realized that he and his fellow laborers were only getting about five hundred calories of food a day. This, he knew, was not enough to sustain life in any man who did heavy manual work. The only solution, he felt, was to expend as little physical energy as possible. He saw his big friend Felix Dumont lose weight rapidly. He saw the smiling good nature gradually leave his face. He warned him to take it easy, to do as little work as possible, and he tried to explain to him something about caloric energy which he had learned at the Oxford school.

One morning as they were marching through the bitter cold from the camp to the plant, Dumont grabbed his arm. "Look," he said in high excitement. Just ahead and to the side of the road were some potato peelings and a few turnips. George bent over, picked up the peelings and the turnips and shoved them into his pocket. A little farther on they saw some more potato peelings and turnips. Dumont shoved these into his shirt pocket with a chuckle.

"We have some friends around here," he whispered to George. "I wonder who they are."

"It is better that we don't know who they are," George said quietly. "The less we know the better for everyone, Dumont." The big man from Bernay nodded thoughtfully.

The Hamburg plant was situated on the Elbe River, and tremendous pressure was exerted upon its four thousand skilled technicians, engineers and forced laborers to keep working at full speed. The final assembling of the submarines was done in concrete underground shelters. For months the Allied bombers had been chipping away at the Hamburg plant, but they had done relatively little damage. Occasionally they'd hit one of the low, squat huts, but within twenty-four hours another would be thrown up and machinery brought from outside and installed. George knew by now that there were a great many Resistance men among the laborers, and for all he knew some British agents, but he couldn't figure out what damage any of them could do to the production of submarines. But they were there for a reason which would be revealed in good time.

One day while shoving his broom slowly across the floor of the plant, a man who had just carried some material into the building whispered tersely, "When the next night raid comes, go out gate No. 3, walk straight ahead two hundred yards. A contact will be there. Say to him, 'It's a bad night.' " Four nights later the warning sirens whined, and within minutes the bombers could be heard approaching. All plant personnel had instructions to go immediately below to shelters. This did not include the forced laborers. Before the first bomb had fallen the skilled personnel and the foreman had hurried below; George and his group of forty found themselves alone in the big shed. Then the night exploded with the hideous sound of bombs landing on the waterfront. George slipped out of the shed. The Hamburg anti-aircraft barrage was perhaps the best in Germany. Thousands of white and purple streaks criss-crossed the sky and the searchlights thrust their long white fingers into the heavens, prying for the Allied planes. They had to fly very high over Hamburg, which made accurate bombing difficult. George found the grounds deserted. He walked toward Gate 3, only a hundred yards from the installation where he worked. To his amazement there wasn't a guard on the gate. The Germans took the order to run for the shelters literally. George walked out of what was usually the best-guarded plant he had ever seen. He crossed the street and went on huddling in the shelter of the buildings. Falling bits of spent shrapnel splattered the pavement around him. He kept on a hundred yards and saw a lone figure half hidden in a doorway. He walked up to him. "It's a bad night," he said, and the man nodded. To George's surprise he spoke in English. He was dressed as a workman but there was no trace of a workman's accent in his speech.

"There are two men in the plant who split diamonds which are used as bearings for submarine instruments," he said. "They are the two best in Europe at this job—Germany has very few men capable of this work. We want their names, addresses and the hours they work. Meet me here during the first raid next week."

George nodded and walked back to the gate. It was still deserted. A dull glow over the city of Hamburg indicated that some of the bombs had found their marks, but none apparently had hurt the huge, sprawling submarine plant. Back in his own installation he looked for Dumont and told him what he wanted.

"Have you contacts in other parts of the plant?" he asked.

The cheerful Dumont nodded. "A dozen of them. I'll pass the word around."

Three days later Dumont came to him with the names, addresses and working hours of the two specialists. They lived in adjoining houses in the suburbs of Hamburg, and they worked at night. Two days later there was another night raid and again George slipped out through the gate. The agent was waiting in the shadows of a doorway. George told him quickly what he had learned. The agent repeated the information slowly and with obvious satisfaction.

"I'll be here every time there is a large-scale raid," he said. "Meet me and I'll have further orders."

A week later Dumont, who by now had been given the job of delivering messages from one part of the plant to another, came to George with exciting news. Wherever he went he picked up bits of gossip and information.

"The Hamburg newspaper today had a story of an unsuccessful British daylight raid," he chuckled. "The German guards were laughing about it. The British Mosquito planes came over but they couldn't even reach the center of Hamburg. The paper said that the anti-aircraft fire was so accurate that the planes jettisoned their bombs on the suburbs and ran for home. Only two houses were hit," Dumont said solemnly. "Two houses on Wilhelmstrasse, just off Bruckenallee."

"And the two diamond splitters?"

"Poor fellows were asleep at the time. They never knew what hit them," Dumont said with mock sorrow.

The night air raids increased. The agent gave George further orders. He had to find the names and addresses of other key men in the plant. The grapevine which now spread all over the huge sprawling plant always furnished the proper information. George heard of specialists who had been killed on their way home from work; he heard of their homes blowing up without benefit of air raids, and the Germans gossiping of such incidents, always within earshot of some Resistance man, attributed such accidents to delayed-action bombs.

"Sink the subs before they get wet," was a policy that was paying off. A group of Norwegians, trusted by the Germans because all professed to be Quislings, helped in the final assembling of the submarines. A submarine was usually launched with a full crew aboard. After it slid down the ways it proceeded ninety-three miles down the Elbe River to the North Sea, where it immediately began its diving tests. The last two subs to be launched had made their first dives, but in each case something had gone wrong with the surfacing apparatus and both subs and their crews had been lost. At last the Germans began to suspect sabotage. Until now they had had such contempt for their half-starved forced laborers that they had looked upon them as animals, incapable of initiative of any kind. It was the job of the Gestapo to furnish these workers, and the military security officers in the factory had always presumed that the Gestapo had done a good screening operation on those they sent to sensitive spots such as this all-important factory. They tightened security measures; they grabbed fifty laborers at random, tortured them in an effort to make them reveal names of Resistance men or agents who were among the workers, but the men they questioned knew nothing of any value to them. By now George realized that he was not the only one who was meeting outside agents and getting orders. There was no central organization in the plant; if an active Resistance man was caught he could say in truth that he did not know the men responsible for the sabotage. George, for instance, knew that Dumont was active, but although occasional messages came to him from other workers, they were usually whispered quickly and then the messenger would fade away. George knew the names of none of those with whom he was working.

The trip to and from hut to factory grew longer each day. The food rations had been cut down and now the men resembled walking skeletons. The ones who were doing heavy manual labor were the first to feel the effects of the unhealthy diet. Within a week three of them died of malnutrition; others barely dragged themselves out of

their cots in the morning. Workers who had out-
lived their usefulness were merely discarded. They
were not shot but were given a medical discharge
and released. They were told to make their way
back to their villages; but they were furnished
neither transport nor food.

The Germans hit upon a new method to dis-
courage sabotage. A third submarine was ready to
be launched, and the forced laborers were ordered
to attend the launching. More than five hundred
of them were lined up alongside. The crew of the
submarine marched aboard. Then an officer called
out ten names. Ten of the workers stepped forward. They were men who had worked on the
final phases of construction, some of them Norwegian keel experts. They were ordered aboard
the sub; they would accompany the U-boat on its
diving tests. The ten men, completely expressionless, climbed the steps which led to the conning
tower. A young Norwegian standing next to George
gripped his arm tightly.

"My father is one of them," he whispered,
choked.

"He'll be all right," George said soothingly.

The young Norwegian shook his head. "No, this
sub has been fixed so that it will never come up
from its first dive." It never did come up.

George DuPre had been in the plant now nearly
ten months—it was February, 1944. One night

when he reported to the outside contact during a raid, he received a rather startling order. The agent handed him a small white pill.

"Take this capsule at eight A.M. tomorrow," he said. "Two hours later report to the doctor."

George nodded. He was anxious to ask questions, but he felt that they wouldn't be answered. He'd survived so far because he had given blind obedience and blind trust to the men in far-off London.

"Is my work here about done?" he did ask.

"Yes, and well done," the agent smiled. "London wants you back in your village. By the way, the effects of the capsule will wear off within twenty-four hours."

The next morning at eight George swallowed the capsule. He waited curiously for the reaction. It wasn't long in coming. First he felt hot, and when he touched his forehead he found it was burning. Then the joints of his arms and legs began to ache. There was a constricted feeling across his chest. Two hours later he had barely the strength to walk to the first-aid shack near the gate. A doctor was in constant attendance. He took George's temperature and then gave a startled exclamation. He put a stethoscope to George's chest and then asked him a few sharp questions. Did his arms and legs ache? George could tell him in all honesty that they did hurt. The doctor muttered something that sounded like "pneumonia." He scribbled George's name and number on a card. He handed it to George with a laconic, "You are unfit to work further. You may leave. This is your pass." George took the little white card in hands which trembled. He stumbled out of the shack. Sentries stopped him at the gate— took one look at him, gave a cursory glance at the card and waved him on. He trudged down the street. Twice he fell from sheer weakness. Slowly he made his way to the outskirts of the city. He felt amazingly light-headed and he had little control over his limbs. Once he was in the farming area outside of Hamburg he stumbled off the road into a field. It was a cold day, but the sweat was pouring from his body. He lay down in the field and slept. When he awoke it was dawn; he must have slept sixteen or seventeen hours. He felt better now except for a languid weakness. But the aches had gone and his brow was no longer fevered. He found that he had picked his field well. Turnips and potatoes were sprouting there. He dug up a few, put them in his pocket and headed toward Torigni, nearly six hundred miles away.

To his surprise he found it fairly easy to hitch-hike. Hitch-hiking was the fashion in Germany. A farmer driving a hay cart would always respond to his uplifted thumb. There were few cars except military ones on the roads. Occasionally he had a real windfall; once a truck picked him up and drove him eighty miles to Hanover. He had no map and little knowledge of the country, but he knew that France lay west and he kept heading in that general direction. There was no reason now for him to maintain his role of village idiot, but he found that he couldn't shake it. When a farmer started to ask him questions he could only drool his answers in the slurred Norman accents of Torigni. He could no longer keep his hands still. They moved constantly in the unco-ordinated fashion typical of an idiot. But gradually he inched his way toward the border. At night he slept in hayracks or slipped into barns. He had survived a severe case of dysentery. He lived off the land, stealing turnips, potatoes, and very occasionally receiving a glass of milk from a kindly woman on a farm. Sometimes he grew faint from hunger. His mouth and the parts afflicted by the sulphuric acid always nagged him with pain, and his feet were torn and blistered. But he kept on doggedly.

He was stopped time after time by military guards and police, but they took one glance at the card which said that he had served ten months at forced labor and had been discharged for medical reasons, and let him pass. It took him three weeks to reach Luxemburg and the French border; it took two more to reach Torigni.

CHAPTER XIII

He arrived in Torigni late in March, 1944. He crawled into the familiar lean-to back of the garage and dropped into a deep sleep. When he awoke the priest and Doctor Rennet were there. The doctor examined him thoroughly.

"You've lost a lot of weight," he said. "But otherwise you're all right. You're going on a vitamin diet for awhile."

Every day he injected large doses of vitamin extract into George's emaciated body. He explained that London had sent him a good supply of drugs, with the vitamins earmarked especially for him. London knew he'd been in bad shape when he returned.

Two weeks after his return the priest brought a

message which electrified him. He was to get the exact measurements of a dozen bridges which spanned canals in the district. It could only mean one thing—invasion. When the Germans retreated they would, of course, blow up all bridges. The invading army would come with bridges of their own, built to exact specifications. George, sustained now by the hope that invasion was near, climbed out of bed to get on with his job. He noticed a difference in the character of the German troops. They were definitely second-raters now; old men and very young men. It seemed apparent that the experienced military men had been sent somewhere else; perhaps to bolster threatened channel ports or beaches. It was absurdly easy to get the measurements of the bridges. No one noticed a half-wit standing on a canal bank with a fish line dangling in the water. George knew the exact length of his improvised fishing pole. He used it as his measuring rod, and every few days the priest would forward the length and width of canal bridges to London.

Then London sent a message asking for every bit of information available on the three German air fields in the vicinity. How many guards were on duty at each field? What time did they change? What type of men were they? How much gasoline was stored at the fields? What type anti-aircraft guns guarded it? George thought this to be a job for the youngsters; the priest had at least twenty of them who were working for the Resistance. He sent them out, and within three days there wasn't anything about the air fields George didn't know. The information was hurried to London.

A further message came. London wanted all the SS uniforms Torigni could capture. The priest ordered his men to ambush an SS truck. The operation proved easy enough. Plenty of Sten guns and grenades had been dropped in recent months. The blacksmith, Innkeeper Benois and Farmer Thibaut hid themselves beside the Saint-Lô road one early morning, and when a truck filled with SS men approached they lobbed grenades at it. The grenades were effective—too effective. The truck was demolished and every SS man riding it was killed, but the uniforms were also destroyed. The Torigni troop (even the priest) never thought of SS men as human beings. By now George shared their view to some extent. The SS organization was like an ugly cancer that had grown upon the body called Germany. Neither George nor any of the troop had any more compunction about killing SS men than a surgeon would have had cutting away a cancerous growth. Their methods of conducting a war by torture had, George felt, disqualified them from being treated as members of the human race. Neither George nor any of the others felt that way about the regular German army. There were occasional examples of extreme cruelty practiced by individual men and officers of the army, but they were isolated cases. In this region at least the army behaved according to the rules; the Gestapo obeyed no rules except the rule of the jungle.

But killing SS men did not provide wearable uniforms. George knew that whenever the weather was good enough the SS men bathed in the nearby streams and in the canals. They undressed, dropped their uniforms on the banks and dove into the water. That's when they were most vulnerable. He told the priest that this was a job that could best be performed by youngsters. They could creep up to the banks, grab the uniforms and run before the startled SS men knew what was happening. They tried it out. Within a week the priest had twelve bright SS uniforms, all in good shape. "Not enough," London said. Regretfully, George said that it was time to use the Sten guns. Many of the youngsters had been clamoring for the chance to use guns. Now when they found a group of SS men bathing, two of the boys with scarves across their faces would appear with the small but deadly guns in their hands. They'd order the bathers to remain in the water. Other youngsters would gather up all the uniforms. When George told London that he now had fifty-six serviceable uniforms of all sizes, London was satisfied.

George expected severe reprisals for the looting

of uniforms, but to his amazement nothing happened. The priest found out that the SS men had been hurriedly shifted closer to the coast. The news spread and the people of Torigni now walked straighter. There was a feeling of expectancy in the air. Then came the never-to-be-forgotten day when the blacksmith rushed from his forge to shout the news that it was D-Day.

There wasn't a German in the village. Georges Lavelle without a word opened a tool box, dug deeply into it and emerged with a bottle of Napoleon brandy. Thibaut rushed to the garage with a bottle of champagne he had been saving for the occasion. Someone started to sing the Marseillaise, and people came in from the fields to join in the chorus. In the midst of the celebration the church bells began to chime happily. The whole village converged on little St. Peter's. Père Gauraud, tears streaming down his face, held a brief thanksgiving service. Then he turned to face his congregation.

"You know the old Normandy saying, 'Don't stop work until the wheat is in the bin.' Our great allies have landed on the beaches," he said, "but remember we are still occupied. When Germans appear don't show your happiness. Do nothing to anger them. We can only wait and pray. Many of you," the priest said earnestly, "are filled with hatred against those who even here in our village have worked these past years with our enemy. Do not

167

take the law into your own hands. We all know who these traitors are. When the British arrive they will be given the names and they will be judged according to law."

The priest was talking to Benois and Thibaut and Baudouin and others who had so often sworn revenge on the collaborators. Even in the hysteria of the celebration his word was law. They did not touch the male collaborators; they did round up the women who had lived with Germans, and to mark them as traitors they cut the hair from their heads.

Two weeks later British reconnaissance cars roared into the village. Benois shouted his greeting and said that his tavern was at their disposal. Some of them tumbled joyfully from the cars to gulp the good wine which Benois had ready. George watched and listened and turned away. He had not been ordered to reveal his identity even to the rescuing forces, and in the absence of such orders he maintained his role. The actual fighting by-passed Torigni; technically the village was still in German hands.

On July 1st an urgent order came for George. He was to hurry to a barn four miles outside the village and remain there for further orders. On the third night Thibaut slipped into the barn. "Follow me, Pierre," he said.

He walked across the Normandy fields, their

stone walls, fences and barn buildings sharply out-
lined in the clear light of a white moon. They
reached a large field and his guide said, "Stay
here." Then he left. George had absolutely no idea
of the next move. Was he off on a new mission? He
hoped not, for his blistered feet were far from well
and he felt as weak as a kitten.

The faint whine of an airplane engine broke the
silence of the lonely night. It grew louder and then
George saw it. A small, single-engined plane cir-
cled the field once and George saw the blinking of
a light across the field. The plane swooped down,
two men appeared from nowhere to grab its wing-
tips and help bring it to a stop. One of them beckoned to him. He hurried across the rough field to
the plane. The door swung open and a grinning
youngster in the uniform of the RAF held out a
helping hand.

"In you get," he said cheerfully.

George stumbled into the plane, it began to
bump across the field, and within a matter of moments it was airborne. The cabin was small but
heated. It had a crew of two, pilot and navigator.
They looked at George and their faces showed their
pity. He was ragged, unshaved, filthy and obviously undernourished. "Have a sandwich," the pilot
said, handing him a package. George unwrapped it.
Two beautiful ham sandwiches were revealed and
he bit into one of them eagerly. The ham was so

heavily spread with French mustard that he couldn't taste it. French mustard was one of the few things there had been no real shortage of during the past four years. In Torigni they had fairly smothered the horse meat with mustard in an effort to disguise its rancid flavor. George found that the taste of the mustard nauseated him.

"Some tea here, too," the pilot said, handing him a thermos bottle. He gulped the hot tea ecstatically. He hadn't tasted tea since 1940. The little plane hedgehopped toward the French coast, but George still had no idea as to where he was being flown, and the habit of abstaining from questions was so strong that he didn't ask the pilot his destination. Then below he saw the Channel and his heart gave a leap. The plane shot up now and the pilot gave it the full throttle. Then they were across the Channel, and looking down George saw a lane of small lights. The plane landed as lightly as a bird upon a wave, and George put his feet on English soil. Two officers were waiting for him. Each grabbed an arm. "I'm all right," he laughed shakily. They led him to the main airport building.

CHAPTER XIV

"May I ask where I am?"

One of the officers chuckled. "You can ask anything you want. You're at Bournemouth, and I'm the C.O. of this station. You're on your way to London."

They led him into the mess. He had hardly been seated before a bowl of soup was put in front of him. It was filled with vegetables. He gulped it greedily. He spread butter on a piece of white bread and ate it slowly, savoring its flavor.

"They want you in London as soon as possible," the C.O. said.

"I'm ready."

They walked outside. Another plane was waiting with its engines idling. George climbed aboard.

Half an hour later the plane landed at Northolt, an airport near London. Again George was greeted by two RAF officers. They hurried him to a car and he was sped toward the capital. The pale night was thinning now and the sun came up just as the car shot through Trafalgar Square. It turned into the Strand, then stopped in front of the Savoy Hotel. "Wait until they see me in here," George said, laughing.

"Oh, they're used to us at the Savoy," the officer said. "We keep a suite here."

They walked into the lobby of the Savoy. It was six A.M. and cleaning women were on their knees scrubbing the floor. The elevator man nodded respectfully to the officer and then they were shot up to the sixth floor. They walked along the long corridor and his guide knocked on a door. It was opened by a cheerful-looking RAF squadron leader. "DuPre? I'm John Appleby. Come in, get rid of those clothes and have a bath." George blinked at the spaciousness of the high-ceilinged apartment. It was one of the Savoy's finest "embankment" suites overlooking the Thames. There were two bedrooms, an enormous living room and two huge bathrooms.

Appleby grinned. "You must be tired of those clothes."

He led him into one of the bedrooms. He helped George peel the filthy, oil-stained clothes from his body. "There's the bathroom," he pointed. "You'll find everything a man can want after an experience like yours."

George walked into the bathroom. Appleby had already filled the tub with hot water. George lowered himself into it. The tension went out of him like air going out of a punctured tire. Now he believed that he was out of France, really believed it for the first time. He lowered himself under the water and wallowed in the luxuriousness of its warmth. He reached for a bar of white soap and lathered his head. He laughed as he watched the water turn a dark gray. He pulled out the plug, emptied the tub and allowed fresh water to fill it. There was a knock on the door and a cheerful yell, "May I come in?"

The smiling squadron leader came in carrying a huge white fleecy robe. "I got rid of those clothes of yours. You'll find everything you need in the bedroom, including a couple of new uniforms. Now tell me, DuPre, do you want water or soda?"

"In what?" George asked.

"Damn it, man, in your Scotch. Where are your eyes? See what's beside you."

There was a small table next to the tub. On it was a bottle of Haig and Haig, a glass, a pitcher of ice and a siphon of soda. "Soda," George said weakly.

Appleby, chatting cheerfully, poured him a

drink. George sipped it slowly. He had never been much of a drinker; this in fact was perhaps the only alcoholic drink he had ever truthfully enjoyed in his life.

"Nothing like the Savoy bathrooms," Appleby said. "Look at those towels; they're about seven feet square, and you'll notice that they're hanging on a heated stand. And there's a telephone. Only hotel I ever heard of that served telephones in the bathrooms. Better not use it, though," he said casually, "until the brass gets through questioning you. You see this medicine cabinet? Well, your kit is there."

"You treat a man pretty well," George smiled.

"I guess you haven't been treated too well these past few years, from what I hear," Appleby said, his face sober. "One thing about this service of ours, if you do return they lay it on for you. While you're here you can order anything the hotel has in the way of food or drink. You want a car and driver? Just yell and it's yours. . . . Hell, there's somebody at the door."

He left to return with a uniformed man carrying a black bag. He introduced himself as an Air Force doctor. "When you're through with that tub, let me have a look at you." He smiled.

He took more than a look. George lay on his bed for an hour while the doctor examined him. "You need a little repair work," he said, and then added dryly, "both north and south. But for the moment

I'm going to give you something to make you sleep. Sleep for eight hours and then I'll let these cloak-and-dagger characters question you. Get between those sheets."

He slept late the next morning and indulged in the incredible luxury of having breakfast in bed. But the huge bathtub drew him like a magnet. He hurried through breakfast and wallowed in the soapy water. The Scotch and the siphon were still on the small table beside the tub. He reached out and poured himself a drink. It was the first time in his life he had ever had a drink in the morning. He laughed as he thought how shocked Muriel would be. There was a knock on the door and he called, "Come in."

The door opened and a hearty voice said, "Glad you're all right, DuPre."

George looked up and recognized the man as the popular Brigadier Matthew Penhale, one of Canada's ranking officers. Should he stand up and salute? What was the etiquette, anyway? There was probably no precedent for finding yourself in a bathtub, a drink in your hand and a big, beribboned General standing over you.

"A fine Canadian you are, drinking Scotch," the Brigadier boomed. "We come from a rye country. If this gets out back home, you'll be in trouble."

"Actually I don't like Scotch much," George said weakly.

"Couple of MI officers here to talk to you, DuPre," Penhale said. "This isn't my show. I just came around to see how a fellow Canadian was doing. I see you're doing all right."

Ten minutes later George, wrapped in his robe, was being questioned by two Brigadiers and a Colonel of British Intelligence.

His answers came haltingly. Sometimes quite involuntarily he answered in French. Occasionally he found himself repeating, *"Je ne sais pas"*; the personality of Pierre Touchette was so much a part of him that he couldn't shake it loose. Warm, sympathetic Brigadier Penhale sensed the mental conflict George was suffering.

"Take it easy, man," he said. "You're tired and confused."

"That's for sure," George said, and the Brigadier laughed.

"Now you're talking like a true Western Canadian," he said.

The doctor stood by watching George closely. Occasionally George caught himself moving his hands aimlessly as he had done for so long. He tried to keep his hands still, tried to look at the officers with the calm eyes of George DuPre, and tried to keep his lower jaw from dropping. It was a tremendous effort. They put beautiful food in front of him, but when he tried to eat it he became violently ill.

"A nervous stomach," the doctor said. "That will pass."

"Take it easy for a day or two," one of the intelligence officers smiled. "We'll be back."

They did come back to ask him a few further questions and to explain the security rules to him. "You may live to be a hundred, DuPre," the Brigadier said. "Even if you do, never mention the name of the town in which you operated. Never mention the names of the eight Resistance men and women with whom you worked. Never mention the code we used in communicating with each other."

George nodded. He didn't quite see the necessity for the secrecy, but he was so accustomed to obeying orders that it never occurred to him to question one.

"We're an old service," the Brigadier mused. "There is a continuity about our end of it. We work in peace and in war. You can tell your story. You can tell it all, but disguise the name of the village and of the eight who worked with you. May seem a bit over-cautious, but," he added casually, "we made this rule back in the Boer War days and it's worked out pretty well in the long run."

"You think you may need the services of the priest and the garage keeper and the others again some time?" George asked.

"You never know," the Brigadier answered.

"Silly business we're in, isn't it? Always getting ready for the next war. We tell ourselves that the next war will never come—but it always does come. Up to now, anyway. Now we'll turn you over to the medicos."

Then they turned him over to the doctor. The doctor told him that the service maintained a hospital at Taplo-on-Thames near Maidenhead, and the medicos there were waiting for him.

"You need some plastic surgery done on your mouth," the doctor said, "and some extensive repairs to your rear end. But we've learned an awful lot about plastic surgery these past few years; they'll make you as good as new. And that nose of yours—who set that broken bone, a butcher?"

"A Gestapo man with a flat face," George said. "He broke it once and reset it twice with the same fist."

"Well, the men at Taplo will take care of it," he said. "Incidentally, you can trust the doctors there one hundred per cent. They send the first team to take care of men in your service."

Two days later George was on the operating table at the small, cheerful hospital on the Thames. They had to remove a great deal of tissue that had been seared by the acid and replace it with new skin. Oral surgeons removed all of his upper teeth. The gums and the bone below were badly infected as a result of the boiling water. They had to scrape the infected bone and do further skin grafting. It seemed to George as though he were commuting from hospital room to operating table, but so skilled were these medicos in the use of anaesthetics that he seldom felt any real pain. They removed the smashed cartilage and bone fragments from his nose, and tried to clear the breathing passages, but they told him he'd have to undergo another operation in a few months to complete the job. They couldn't do anything about the scar on his chin where he had been slashed by the heavy ring of the Gestapo sergeant.

A psychiatrist was on constant duty at Taplo, and between operations he sat at George's bedside encouraging him to talk. "I guess you're the only one on the staff whose services I don't require," George said one day to the doctor.

"Forget I'm a doctor," the psychiatrist laughed. "Sometimes a man who comes back from a long trip abroad likes to have an audience. Well, George, I'm your audience. I'm completely classified, so don't worry about spilling any of your precious secrets."

"Mentally I'm as good as ever," George said, and only the experienced doctor detected the shrill note in his voice.

"Of course you are," the psychiatrist soothed. "All you have to do is to forget Pierre Touchette and remember that you are George DuPre. Half the time you talk like Pierre Touchette, you know," he added casually.

"Funny," George muttered, "I have to learn how to act like myself all over again."

CHAPTER XV

By April, 1945, George felt physically well again. Daily vitamin injections had cured the malnutrition and anemia from which he quite unknowingly had been suffering. The new gum tissue had grown healthy and strong, and he had become accustomed to the plate which the dentists had so skillfully fashioned. The miracle of plastic surgery had replaced the tissue destroyed by the sulphuric acid. He still was apprehensive about straightening up suddenly, for sometimes the new skin had a tendency to ache when stretched, but on the whole he felt well. His breathing was fairly good again; a second operation would bring his breathing back to normal.

"It's time I got out of here," he told the psychiatrist. "I'm a healthy man now; I'm just filling a bed that someone else might need."

"You're restless," the doctor mused. "You don't sleep well."

"I'm not accustomed to lying in a bed or walking in a garden," George said a bit irritably.

"All right, then," the doctor spoke crisply, as though he had made a decision. "The MI-5 boys have been after me. They want you to do what they call 'just one small job of work' for them. I've kept them away. . . ."

"Anything," George said eagerly. "This inactivity is driving me batty."

"Perhaps some real work to occupy your mind will help," the doctor said thoughtfully. "All right. You can go to London tomorrow."

One of the Brigadiers who had questioned George at the Savoy received him with smiles. "You look like a new man, DuPre," he said. "They work wonders down there at Taplo."

"Yes, sir, but I'm still on active duty," George said, "and my idea of active duty isn't sitting around a hospital. Especially when I'm as fit as ever."

"All right," the Brigadier said. "We have a job for you. It shouldn't take more than a month and then it's back to Canada for you. Sit down and I'll tell you about it."

He explained the military situation in Germany.

The Allies were driving on Berlin. It was only a matter of weeks before the capital fell, and that in effect would mean the end of the war. The Allies had already announced that the German war criminals would be tried by a military tribunal as soon as hostilities ceased. Hundreds of high-ranking Gestapo and army officers, as well as Nazi political leaders, were on the list of those who would not be treated as ordinary war prisoners but rather as members of a conspiracy which had deliberately launched World War II.

"These men know they're for it once they're captured," the Brigadier said. "And a great many of them have already deserted the German forces and have found refuge in German prisoner-of-war camps."

"I don't get it," George said, puzzled.

"Those who speak English well get hold of British, American or Canadian uniforms," the Brigadier explained. "With or without the connivance of prison officials they get into the compounds where they pass themselves off as Allied officers. Many of them are brilliant at deceiving prisoners who might even come from the same part of the country they claim to come from. And so they are accepted. As soon as we liberate these camps we will, of course, hurry all prisoners back here to England. Once they arrive here these masqueraders will have no trouble getting lost. These high-ranking Germans

183

all have plenty of money salted away. Where? Argentina, Switzerland, Sweden—everywhere. They will have provided themselves with proper identity papers and off they'll go to Southern Ireland or Spain or God knows where."

"Are they in the prison camps now?"

"Oh, yes. Matter of fact, Squadron Leader Bushell, who is chairman of the escape committee at Stalag 3 in the Berlin area, believes that there are at least thirty Germans hiding in his camp."

"He's a prisoner and you keep in touch with him?" George asked.

"Good heavens, yes." The Brigadier looked surprised. "Been in communication with him for a couple of years. He felt that many of these fakers in his camp were masquerading as Canadians. He asked us to drop a few of you chaps in the vicinity of Stalag 3. You'd be picked up, taken to the camp, and you could spot the real from the bogus Canadians."

"No one who wasn't a Canadian could fool one of us," George said with certainty.

"I don't know," he frowned. "Sampson has some of your countrymen with him and they've okayed most of these chaps. But he still is suspicious. His fellow prisoners are strictly combat men who haven't had the training that—well—that you've had. We're sending two Canadians over there soon.

Now after what you've been through I don't want to ask . . ."

"I'd love to go along." For the first time in months DuPre felt alive.

"Well, that's settled." The Brigadier picked some papers from his desk. "Read this material. This is a list of every Canadian outfit over here. On this paper you'll find the names of the regiments which took part in the Dieppe show, and here are those who were with Monty when he took Catania in Sicily. This list gives the names of the three Canadian regiments which landed on D-Day, with the names of various commanding officers. Here's another list. It shows the names of every vessel used to transport Canadians. Some ships were torpedoed; others were transferred to the Pacific. I'd better send you to the Savoy to your old suite and let you spend two days with all this. That should be enough. Baker," he added casually, "says you have a good memory. By the way, you'll go in uniform this time. You'll be an air gunner for the purpose of this trip."

"Two days will be enough," George said.

It was. Three days later a car picked him up and took him to a bombing station. He met six men who were going along on the mission. They received precise instructions. The pilot would simulate a crash landing in a field some thirty miles southwest of Berlin.

"Won't be a bad landing, chaps," the pilot laughed. "I know the field well. And the Lancaster won't be heavily loaded."

DuPre found that two of his colleagues were Canadians; Flight Lieutenant Theodore "Tug" Wilson, and Flying Officer Fred Hutchinson. The huge Lancaster took off at midnight, aiming to make the simulated crash landing at dawn. It flew nicely through the dark night, and not a bit of flak was hurled at them during the long trip. "The Jerries are short of ammo," the pilot explained cheerfully. "And they never send anything up at a single aircraft. They don't even send fighters up after a lone plane. This flight will be nothing but a piece of cake."

The pilot was right. The plane, carrying nothing but seven men, was light enough to fly high, and the weather was good. George and his fellow Canadians dozed off and then the pilot told them to hang on; they were going in. The plane swooped down, touched the large field and bumped across it. It came to a stop and then the crew began to destroy instruments and get rid of papers—all completely worthless. The men tumbled out of the big bomber. The dawn broke now to reveal a tidy countryside. George and the two Canadians, according to pre-arranged plans, lit out together. They didn't light out very fast. They sat on the side of a nearby road as though bewildered and stunned by the impact of the crash. Within a few moments four policemen, headed by a rather frightened little rolypoly official, pounced on the three Canadians. The official, highly excited, announced that he was the Mayor of the small village outside of which the plane had crashed, and he added that they were his prisoners.

George had been worried only about one thing. He knew that the German people, maddened by the incessant bombing, had more than once taken out their bitter resentment against downed Allied fliers by killing them instead of turning them over to military authorities. The little Mayor was too proud of his catch to allow any civilians to interfere. He marched them to a police station in the village and sent for the military. They were interrogated, and they answered freely. Flak had put two of their engines out of commission, they said, and they had crash-landed. They were immediately hustled to Stalag 3, the huge P.O.W. camp only a few miles away. They showed the right amount of dejection, and only looked sheepish when the Germans taunted them about the loss of their plane. The attitude of the Germans suprised George. They weren't friendly, but they had lost all of their arrogance and confidence. They knew the game was up and now they were meticulous in their behavior toward prisoners. Registered at the camp, they went through the routine of further questioning and then they were assigned to barracks. The prisoners pounced on them eagerly. They were half starved, but were more hungry for news than for food. Late that afternoon the three were conducted to Squadron Leader Bushell. Bushell, tall, thin-faced, wielded the same authority here at the camp as he would have at an RAF base. His word was law. No escape plan could be launched unless he had approved of it. He dealt with any infractions of the rules which the prisoners themselves had drawn up. Stalag 3 was a well-organized camp.

Bushell welcomed the three Canadians and told them where they would find their countrymen. They usually gathered together in the afternoon in one corner of the stockade. He gave them the names of those whom he suspected. He was especially interested in one Flying Officer Harlan Drew, even though Drew had been accepted by his fellow Canadian prisoners. He told George to concentrate on him. The three established contact with the Canadian prisoners the following day. George ran into men from his part of the country, and the reunion was a happy one. The prisoners of war were sustained by the certainty that the fall of Berlin was imminent and that they'd soon be released. Many had been languishing in prison camps since the ill-fated Dieppe raid in August, 1942.

"They're treating us pretty well here," one of the Canadians laughed. "Hoping that we'll put in some good words for them later on."

"Will you?"

"Not bloody likely," he said bitterly. "A year ago they were singing a different tune."

DuPre was introduced to all the Canadians. Finally he heard the name Flying Officer Harlan Drew. Drew was a bulky man with a frank, open-faced smile. "Bad luck," he said, "getting nipped just when it's about over," he said sympathetically. George wondered briefly if the Squadron Leader could be wrong. The man had the accent of the Canadian; he looked like a Canadian and he seemed a decent fellow. Then George caught himself up sharply. Here he was—feeling when he should be thinking. Likes, dislikes, personalities, charm, apparent decency—these were not the qualities to consider. He chatted with Drew and managed to meet him often during the following days. George was a good listener and Drew was in a talkative mood. He had joined the RCAF in Brandan, Manitoba, he said. He'd had his basic training at Edmonton, Alberta, and had then gone to Rivers, Manitoba, for flight instruction.

"I just didn't have it," he said ruefully. "After I'd washed out two Harvard trainers they told me I was a ham-handed bum. So they transferred me to navigation. Actually I was thirty-five then, a bit old for flying. I'd taken eight years off my age to get into the flying end of it. They sent me to Halifax for navigational training, and I found that this was my field all right."

George knew Rivers and Edmonton, and he knew Halifax, and it soon became evident that Drew knew them just as well as he did. If ever a man seemed to be genuine it was this big, thirty-nine-year-old smiling giant.

"When did you get to England?" George asked casually.

"December, 1942," Drew answered. "And I'll never forget that trip. We were in convoy and the damn subs were on our tail the whole way. Got two of our ships, too. But not the old *Bayano*. She was only 14,000 tons, but she rode out hurricanes and ducked submarines beautifully."

He chatted on, but George was seeing the list of transports he had studied so intensively at the Savoy. The ships had been listed alphabetically. He remembered the brief note under the "B" 's— "*S. S. Bayano*—14,000 tons—built in Scotland— 1924. Used as Atlantic transport 1940, 1941. Then transferred April 15, 1941, to United States for use in the Pacific. Since then has served in Pacific area."

"You landed in 1942 on the *Bayano*?" George's tone was casual.

"Yes, we landed at Liverpool," Drew said. "Damn good pub there—the Adelphi. They've got an American bar in that hotel as good as anything you'd find in Montreal."

George smiled as he nodded, but he knew that sooner or later a rope would be placed around this man's neck. That afternoon he reported to Squadron Leader Bushell. During the next three weeks DuPre and his two Canadian colleagues turned in a dozen names to the Squadron Leader of men they had caught in contradictions or lies. In all, the Squadron Leader had a list of twenty-two Germans who had resorted to this unorthodox method of escaping the consequences of their war crimes.

"Who they actually are I don't know," the Squadron Leader said. "But they must be high-ranking Gestapo, Nazi or army men. Only the high-ranking chaps have had the education to make themselves bi-lingual. Not one of these men has betrayed himself by his accent. Incidentally, DuPre, London is very pleased at what you've done here."

"London knows already?"

"I'm in touch with London," the Squadron Leader laughed. "Incidentally, the Americans will be here in a few days. It's all over now but the shouting. And you'll be hurried back to London immediately."

A week later the camp commanders fled, the Americans did arrive and their Colonel immediately searched out the Squadron Leader, DuPre, and a dozen others—men who were apparently agents like George. They were flown back to England. Shortly afterwards the men from Stalag 3 were shipped to Bournemouth and George was sent there with the Squadron Leader, Tug Wilson and Fred Hutchinson, to identify the Canadian masqueraders. All were rounded up and all stood trial at Nuremberg later on.

CHAPTER XVI

DuPre was ordered back to the hospital for one more nose operation. It was a simple operation, but they kept him at Taplo. He fretted at the confinement. He'd felt fine while he was at Stalag 3, but there he'd had something to occupy his mind. Here it was different. Now the nightmares returned; the nervous stomach came back to plague him.

The psychiatrist tried to curb his restlessness.

"You've been through more than you realize, George," he said earnestly. "And damn it, man, your reaction to it all just isn't normal. I know you want to get out of here. You're beginning to think of this hospital as a place of confinement. Somehow you identify it with—well—say, the veterinary hospital in Saint-Lô or other prisons or interrogation centers."

George looked at him sharply. This man could read his mind. "I just get restless," George muttered. "I come from the north country. In Canada we aren't accustomed to being hemmed in."

"All right, George. I'll let you go tomorrow on one condition. I want you to phone me at ten o'clock every morning to tell me how you feel. Okay?"

"Sure, it's okay," George laughed. "But it seems rather silly."

"Well, humor the whim of an old doctor. We have some friends down in Derbyshire," he added casually. "They own a big estate; plenty of room even for a Canadian. Why not spend a few weeks down there? It's lovely country. Do a little gardening; do a lot of walking, and there's no reason why we can't ship you back home pretty soon."

Two days later George found himself living in one of England's finest old homes. His host and hostess were gracious and understanding.

It was the home of the Marquis of Keddlestone, an army major who had just been mustered out of service. He and his wife treated George as though he were a member of the family. He had a large room and bath of his own. The room looked out over the lovely rolling Derbyshire countryside, and George felt that it wouldn't be long before he was fully recovered. The Marquis encouraged him to talk of his early life at army posts. The memories were becoming more real all the time; Torigni and the past four years were gradually beginning to assume unreality. His waking mind was able to forget Torigni; it was only at night, when his subconscious took over and the nightmares gripped him, that Torigni intruded.

He took the advice of the doctor; he wandered all over the thickets and streams of the big estate. Each morning at ten he phoned Taplo. "I'm feeling fine, Doc," he'd say, and the psychiatrist would give him a cheerful, "Good, George, that's all I want to know." An ancient gardener had by some horticultural miracle kept the flower beds blooming despite the shortage of help. George puttered around the garden with the old man, listening to him talk lovingly of the roses which had won prizes for him before the war. One morning George awoke with a strange compulsion. He wanted to cut the hedge that bordered the formal flower beds. He gulped a quick breakfast and then hurried to the gardener's shed. He told the old man what he wished to do. The gardener gave him a heavy pair of shears. George almost ran to the hedge. It really needed clipping, he told himself happily. He set to work methodically. It was a warm day and he began to perspire. But he kept at it, never stopping for a moment. It was nearly mid-morning when the gardener came over to inspect his work.

"That's fine, sir," he said a little doubtfully. "Just fine. But take it easy. Here it is nearly eleven and you've been at this since nine without a rest."

George didn't hear him. His eyes were fastened almost hypnotically on the flashing blades of the shears. Snip . . . snip . . . snip they went, and now the sun glanced off the bright blades and George's head began to fill with strange fancies. He saw the flat face of the Gestapo sergeant between the blades, and he snipped faster and faster. He didn't feel the ache in his arms. He only knew that he had to hurry; he had to move the shears faster and faster. He saw the boy Armand Owens standing before the firing squad, and he knew that there was only one way to save him; he had to work the shears even faster. He didn't hear the worried voice of the gardener. He didn't see him run toward the house, nor did he know that his host was on the phone now talking to the Taplo psychiatrist. His arm muscles were screaming in protest but he cried, "Hurry, hurry," and now he was opening and closing the blades of the shears as quickly as he could. He had to hurry or they'd shoot Armand . . . Now they were closing in on the little priest, and only he could save him. There was a roaring in his ears and then suddenly the shears fell from his hands; he swayed forward and collapsed against the hedge which he had cut almost down to the roots.

The ambulance came and sped him back to Taplo. He was carried to his old room. For five days he lay there unconscious, part of his mind fighting madly to reassert the personality of Pierre Touchette, while the other fought to re-establish George DuPre. When he awoke it was to find himself in a warm bath. A uniformed attendant was watching him closely.

"You're awake?" he asked.

George nodded. What was he doing in a bathtub? He turned his head to ask a question, but the effort was too much for him. When he awoke again he was in bed and someone was bending over him.

"I'm all right now?" George asked weakly.

"You will be. But you need a quiet month or so . . ."

Every day they slung him into a hammock which was suspended into a bathtub. He lay there with the warm water swirling around him. He found it much easier to think clearly as the warmth penetrated his body and relaxed his muscles and quieted his nerves. He spent three hours every day in the warm bath, and now he could sleep without the horror of the nightmares. The doctor allowed him to walk around the grounds, but he found that he tired easily.

Every morning the psychiatrist would sit with him, encouraging him to talk of his early days in Canada, of his happy years in the North. The doctor never mentioned Pierre Touchette. He was trying gently but persistently to make his patient completely recapture the mind and personality of George DuPre.

"Did you ever take your wife to the North country?" he asked George, and quite unconscious of the fact that he was being treated by the brilliant psychiatrist, George would launch happily into memories of those wonderful days.

"We had a log cabin in Northern Manitoba," George said. "Muriel and I. We spent three years there. I was supervising the trappers who were catching muskrat. This was a government muskrat preserve, you know. Just a one-room cabin we had, on a huge island. On one side was the Summerberry River; on the other the Saskatchewan. The nearest settlement was eighty miles away at Thepas; mostly Indians there. In the summer we'd go to Thepas once or twice. I had a canoe with an outboard motor. That seems so long ago."

Every day the doctor would get George to talk about his life in the North. It was hard at times for George to remember. He remembered the important things, though. Just before the annual freeze he and Muriel would stock up for the long winter. They'd shoot grouse and ptarmigan, ducks, geese, and there would always be a side of venison hanging outside the cabin. Deer and moose were plentiful as long as you could shoot a .303 Remington.

"Are you a good shot, George?" the doctor asked.

"My wife thought for a time that I was the best

shot in the world," George laughed. "One day a hawk was flying overhead carrying a small field mouse in its claws. I only had a .22 with me. I said, 'Honey, anyone can hit a hawk with a rifle, but it takes a genius to hit a small mouse that the hawk is carrying. Now just watch.' Well, Doctor, I shot my rifle and darned if the hawk didn't drop that field mouse right at our feet. Muriel was astounded. She didn't know then that if you shoot within four feet of a hawk the bird gets frightened and drops anything he's carrying. She learned later, though."

"Would you ever go to the settlement in the winter?"

George nodded. "We had a dog team. We'd go right down the frozen river. The first trip was always exciting; that's when you found out how your new dogs were. You raised them and trained them, but until you got them in harness pulling a sled you were never sure."

He told the doctor of poker games in Thepas in which the pelts of white foxes were used instead of money. "If two men had good hands, they'd just stack their pelts on the table," George told him. "As though they were chips. One night everyone dropped out but two men. One man ran out of pelts, but he still wanted to bet. He said, 'My schooner, *Annabelle*, is frozen in at the wharf. I'll bet that against the rest of your pelts.' So it was agreed. They lay down their hands. The man with the pelts had a royal flush. Without a word the loser got up from the table, went out the door, walked to his schooner and picked up a can of paint. He painted out the word *Annabelle* and under it painted *Royal Flush*. The *Royal Flush* is still up there, going up and down the Saskatchewan."

George was feeling better every day. The nights were long, especially when nightmares awoke him, and he'd lie in bed, every muscle tense, until the realization that he was not in France but in a bed in a white room in a hospital on the Thames relaxed him. Then, too, he still had his nervous stomach. But he was losing the look and the mannerisms of Pierre Touchette.

One day he asked the doctor what had caused his breakdown; why had he been compelled to wield those shears so frantically until he had collapsed.

"It was the best thing in the world that could have happened," the doctor said. "The thing I've been waiting to happen. That's why I insisted that you phone me at ten each morning. When you didn't phone I hurried an ambulance right over there. You see, George, you thought you were all right. Well, you were all right, but your subconscious didn't realize that it was all over and that you were completely well and safe. All during your convalescence you were just too damn normal, George. Men who've lived for nearly five years under the horrible strain that you've endured just aren't supposed to act as normal and composed as you've been. Actually, it is normal to have a nervous reaction."

"Is that what I had?" George asked weakly.

The doctor nodded. "A layman would say that you had a delayed reaction. Leave it at that, George."

"Will it happen again?"

"No reason why it should. Let's put it this way, though my learned colleagues who go in for technical jargon would be horrified at my explanation —let's say that your subconscious finally realized that you were free and safe and your subconscious was so damn happy about it that it held a private celebration that completely upset the well-ordered conscious part of your mind. And so the mental explosion."

"What happens now?"

"You feel a little weak, don't you, George? Of course. That's only natural. You might say that you've had a mental cathodic. You'll be weak for a little while and then you'll feel fine. This I can promise, George. And another thing—don't bottle everything up in that subconscious of yours. You can put only so much strain on your mind and then it rebels."

George nodded thoughtfully. This doctor was a wise man.

"Another thing," the doctor said. "This isn't my

department, but I've been looking over your chart. When you joined up you weighed 179 pounds. When you arrived here from France you weighed 127 pounds. Since then you've gained ten pounds, but I think we should add a bit of meat to you. You don't want to scare your wife by looking like a skeleton."

The doctor was right. Within two weeks he was George DuPre again. The personality of Pierre Touchette had been ejected from his subconscious by the "mental cathodic." His speech was becoming clearer and his hands seldom moved aimlessly in the manner of the idiot garage helper. His diet and injections had put another ten pounds on him.

They allowed him to write to his wife, saying that he was on his way home, and then one day he was driven to Liverpool and put on a ship. He was landed at Norfolk, Virginia, and put on a train headed for Canada. The trip seemed to last forever, but finally there came the never-to-be-forgotten moment when George DuPre stepped off the train in the glare of a hot Winnipeg sun, and then his wife's arms were around him and for the first time in nearly six years everything was all right.

"But, darling, your hair has turned white," she said.

"It's that English sun," he laughed.

The gentle spy was home.

POSTSCRIPT

There is nothing at all to distinguish George DuPre from his neighbors in Calgary, where he now lives. As branch manager of Commercial Chemicals he is just another business man in the fast-growing Western Canadian city. Few of his neighbors or business associates know how he spent the war years. They left no visible marks on him. The battered nose has been completely restored by plastic surgery. There is a scar where the heavy ring on the hand of the Gestapo sergeant opened the flesh, but even that is fading.

Since his return DuPre has fathered two sons; David George, who is six, and Glenn Maurice, who is five. They are much more interested in their cowboy suits and their toy guns than they are in a war that took place before they were born. They are very close to their father and are proud of the badge he wears in his coat lapel at all times. They know this means that their father is an official of the Boy Scouts; both wait anxiously for the day when they are old enough to become Scouts.

George and Muriel live quietly, in perfect understanding. She never asks George about those years during which he lived another man's life, a forgotten, pathetic creature named Pierre Touchette. Sometimes George says that he won't be home for dinner, and she knows then that there is a Boy Scout meeting somewhere and she knows that except for herself and the children this is the most important thing in the world to her husband. She has heard him speak to the Scouts and she has seen the rapt attention they give him, and she knows that this is a good thing not only for the boys but for her husband.

DuPre is a quiet man who listens more than he talks. "Anyone ever tell you that you look like a smaller edition of Eisenhower?" men often ask, meeting him for the first time. DuPre smiles and says, "That's a good man to look like." His hair is white and he has an engaging grin. His eyes are clear and blue, and his face has the tanned appearance which is the heritage of his years in the Arctic. When he talks to the Boy Scouts he does it in the informal manner youngsters like. He tells them a few of the things that happened to him, and then he talks about Canada.

"I'm not a preacher," he says earnestly, "but I'll tell you boys one thing. I never met a brave man during the war who didn't believe in God. You can't have guts without God, boys; that's the one lesson the war taught me. But I'm not going to preach to you about anything except Canada. You and I are lucky to belong to such a great country. If you are a good Canadian, it follows automatically that you are a good Christian. You just can't be a patriotic Canadian and not believe in God."

He tells them of the boy Armand Owens, who was their age. His love for his country finally brought him to God, he says, and he tells of how the boy died with the name of the Creator on his lips. They listen with fascination, for George DuPre does not preach to them. His simplicity, his intense sincerity have an amazing effect on the youngsters.

Once a month George attends a meeting of the Canukeena Club, an organization of ex-service men. Its motto is *Non Nobis Solum* (Not for Ourselves Alone), and it is dedicated to helping support the dependents of men who died in the war. Sometimes when the men sit around after dinner discussing the war, George feels a little out of it. They tell of exciting air battles, of the satisfaction of finally securing a difficult beach-head, and George feels that they are talking almost a foreign language. He had none of these experiences.

"I was never in combat," he says sadly when some visiting member, not knowing his background, tries to bring him into the conversation.

George is not the kind of man who can bear inactivity. When he had recovered from his third and final nose operation in the fall of 1946, he wanted to go to work. He had met James C. Barr, president of Commercial Chemicals, Ltd., and Barr asked him if he'd like to join the rising young company as its Branch Manager in Edmonton. The idea suited George, and for two years he and Muriel lived a quiet and happy life in Edmonton. He quickly established contact with the Boy Scouts of the city and was made a member of the Edmonton District Council. Only his very best friends knew his background; it was not something George or Muriel liked to talk about, and then through his Boy Scout activities George met a man whom he reveres above all living souls.

Nathan E. Tanner began life as the son of Mormon parents living in Salt Lake City, Utah. They took him to Canada in a covered wagon in the 1890's, as a child. He grew up as a Mormon, became a Bishop, a teacher, and eventually one of the most respected citizens in the province of Alberta. In 1938 the provincial government plucked him from his teaching position to make him Minister of

Mines for Alberta. Later he was given an additional portfolio—Minister of Lands and Forests. All the natural resources of the mineral-, oil-, land- and forest-rich province were in his care. For fifteen years he protected the resources of Alberta from exploitation, and all political parties had nothing but complete confidence and pride in Nathan E. Tanner, Mormon Bishop and Provincial Commissioner of Boy Scouts.

It was in this later capacity that George DuPre met him. The tall, soft-voiced, highly cultured, handsome Mormon Bishop and the short, slight, "smaller edition of Eisenhower" had much in common. Both were quiet men. Both were religious, although George attended the United Church (a merger of the Presbyterian and Methodist sects). Both were devoted to the Boy Scout ideal, and both were humble men who didn't ask too much of life. DuPre admired the brilliant intellect of the cabinet minister; Tanner admired the simplicity and the integrity of this man who had gone through so much and who hadn't been disillusioned or made bitter by his experiences. In 1949 Tanner felt that he needed someone like George DuPre in his department. Alberta was in the throes of a healthy boom; oil had been discovered and American capital was pouring into the province. Any time huge capital flows into a district, the possibility for corruption increases. Tanner wanted a man who would act as a confidential investigator, a man who quietly and unostentatiously would investigate any complaints. He asked George to take over this job.

"I need you, George," Tanner said simply, and that was quite enough for DuPre.

He was just, as he puts it, "getting his feet wet" in his position as Branch Manager for Commercial Chemicals, but his respect for Tanner equaled the respect he had once held for a man named Baker who headed the training school for agents outside Oxford. George went to James Barr, and when he had explained, Barr put his arm around George's shoulders and said, "If Nathan Tanner needs you, that's enough for us. We feel about him as you do, George. You stay with him until he releases you and then come back to us. There will always be a place with Commercial Chemicals for you, George."

And so George DuPre became a sort of one-man FBI for Nathan Tanner's department. Larceny and the sale of "influence" were the startling exception rather than the accepted custom in Alberta, and although George turned up a few cases of a venal nature, he never had to report anything more widespread. Sometimes he did tell Muriel of amusing incidents. It quickly became known that Tanner trusted him completely, and one day a get-rich-quick promoter who didn't quite know the score in Alberta approached George with a proposition.

"You have to have Tanner's okay to operate up

here," he told George. "Okay. I've operated all over the world and I know the pitch. To see Tanner we have to see you first. That's all right, too. Now I've got a legitimate proposition to lay before Tanner. I represent an American company that is ready to spend three million dollars right now to develop oil properties up here. All I want to do is to get to Tanner. You're his man. Name your price just to get me in to talk to Tanner."

George DuPre never really had the capacity for anger. He was merely amused at this. He said, "Pick up the phone there on my desk. Ask for Mr. Tanner's secretary. Tell her you want to make an appointment with him. Here . . . here's the phone."

The American picked up the phone cautiously. He did as George suggested. The secretary said that the Minister would be glad to see the American representative at ten o'clock the following morning. The American looked puzzled as he hung up.

"You could have made that phone call from Detroit or New York or from wherever you come," George said gently. "You don't have to go through any intermediary to see Mr. Tanner. He and Alberta welcome American corporations to Alberta."

In 1952 Nathan Tanner, after fifteen years of service, resigned from the Government. Shortly afterwards George DuPre too resigned. He went back to see James Barr. "We've been waiting for you, George," the president of Commercial Chemicals said. "We want you back with us. We hoped you'd be back some day, and during the time you were with the Government we kept up your pension payments. You will lose nothing by the leave of absence you've had. That's what we consider it to be. Now, how about taking over as Branch Manager in Calgary for us?"

It was in Calgary that I caught up with George DuPre. He was Branch Manager of Commercial Chemicals, and now the father of two children.

George DuPre is not a leading citizen of Calgary. Very few know that their new neighbor was ever a member of British Intelligence. The good friends he and Muriel have know all about it, but they don't discuss it much. They're too busy with the everyday problems of getting baby sitters for their children when they want to attend a movie in downtown Calgary at night. The people George and Muriel attract as friends are gentle and quiet people like themselves. They see a lot of their neighbor, Colonel William Hamilton, his wife and their five-year-old youngster. Bill Hamilton is Calgary Branch Manager for the National Grain Company. They see a great deal of genial Brigadier Kenneth Lockett, an official of the Crown Seed Company, and his wife. Sometimes one of the ex-RCAF pilots persuades George to drop into the local mess (really a

club), and if you go along with George you'll meet
the local C.O. of the air base, Squadron Leader Ross
Parker, and you'll meet Fred Clarke, who is now an
official of Alberta Distillers, Ltd. During the war he
was a fighter pilot, flying an American Mustang
(P-51).

"You were at Dieppe, weren't you?" he said to
me when I met him with DuPre. I nodded.

"You were on the command ship," he added. "It
was called the *Calpe*. Right?" I nodded, wondering
how he knew this. "Great gunners you had aboard
that ship," he said. "Do you remember mistaking a
Mustang for a Messerschmitt and shooting it down?
The Mustang landed alongside the *Calpe*, and you
chaps fished what you thought to be a German pilot
out of the drink."

"I remember it well," I said. "Our gunners were
very proud of themselves until they found out that
the German pilot was a Canadian and that the
Messerschmitt was a Mustang."

"I'm the Canadian," he laughed. "I figure you
owe me a drink, but damn it, this is our mess and
no strangers are allowed to buy drinks here. George,
how did you ever tangle with this American?"

"He's doing some kind of a story," George said a
little sheepishly, for the thought that his full story
would appear in print was a rather frightening one
to George DuPre.

Calgary is a quiet city, and the permanent residents are quiet men and women who are very
happy with their city and who feel a kind of pity
for those who live in the East—whether it be Eastern Canada or the Eastern United States. Drop into
the excellent Pallisser Hotel, the focal point of all
Calgary social life, and you'll meet other men who
call George DuPre friend. You'll meet smiling Ernie
Locke, district traffic manager of Trans-Canada
Airlines, and brilliant Bob Waldie, who looks too
young to have gone through a war with the Artillery and to have somehow earned a master's degree
in chemistry after the war. His very obvious in-
tellectual talents have been harnessed by Alberta
Distillers, Ltd. (a new industry to Western Canada). And they talk of their children and they
talk with pride of this clean, neat, friendly city in
which they live, but they don't talk much of the
war. That's all past history to these men who did
the fighting; for the most part it is the noncom-
batants who like to discuss the "good old days."
Men who fought never really think of them as
"good old days." They're enjoying the good days
now, doing all right financially, raising families;
Calgary is a city of happy people, and of them all
George DuPre is perhaps the most contented. He's
getting even more out of life than he ever asked. A
wife like Muriel, kids like David and Glenn, the

respect of a man like Nathan Tanner, and the friendship of his Calgary neighbors—George asks quite simply—"What better things has life to offer?"

Sometimes when ex-service men show their hatred and bitterness toward the Germans, George feels uncomfortable. He believes strongly that the Germans were trained to brutality. Left to themselves, even the Gestapo torturers would have ended up as decent enough men. They had to be taught to hate; their decent feelings had to be rooted out of them by years of pressure. Then they became nothing but animals, much like Pavlov's dogs, responding only to conditioned reflexes.

DuPre feels no bitterness at all, not even toward those who tortured him. If youngsters all over the world grew up as Boy Scouts are growing up in Canada today, George feels that future wars would be impossible. Decent, God-fearing kids grow up into decent, God-fearing men, and he doesn't think for a moment that decent men could ever war on one another.

DuPre has nothing but contempt for force as a weapon. It couldn't even work successfully against the people of a tiny village like Torigni. Understanding each other is the only way to permanent peace, George argues strongly. Russia? If the Russians were to have their faith restored to them they'd be like the rest of us, he says.

"Neither an individual nor a nation can get very far without believing in God," George DuPre says earnestly, and then he smiles apologetically, "I don't mean to preach. I'm just not the preaching type."

QUENTIN REYNOLDS' career as a war correspondent is well known to millions of American readers. His books, articles, broadcasts, films and lectures did more to arouse popular support in America for Britain's cause than all the official communiqués and propaganda combined. Among his best-known wartime books were *Only the Stars Are Neutral, Dress Rehearsal, The Wounded Don't Cry* and, postwar, *Leave It to the People*.

Since the end of the war, Mr. Reynolds has been editor of *United Nations World*, has written numerous articles for such magazines as *Life* and *Reader's Digest*, and is a regular member of the panel on the TV show, "It's News to Me." In addition to all these activities, Mr. Reynolds wrote the highly successful *Courtroom, The Amazing Mr. Doolittle* and *I, Willie Sutton*. Recently, this prolific author ventured into the children's book field and his *The Wright Brothers, Custer's Last Stand* and *The Battle of Britain* are best sellers in Random House's fabulously successful Landmark Series.